image grammar
ACTIVITY BOOK

HARRY R. NODEN

Perfection Learning®

Editorial Director   Julie A. Schumacher
Designer   Emily J. Greazel
Image Acquisition   Anjanette Miner

© Copyright 2007 by Perfection Learning® Corporation
1000 North Second Avenue
P.O. Box 500
Logan, Iowa 51546-0500
Tel: 1-800-831-4190 · Fax: 1-800-543-2745
perfectionlearning.com

Printed in the United States of America

5 6 7 RD 12 11

ISBN 10: 0-7891-7082-5
ISBN 13: 978-0-7891-7082-8

CONTENTS

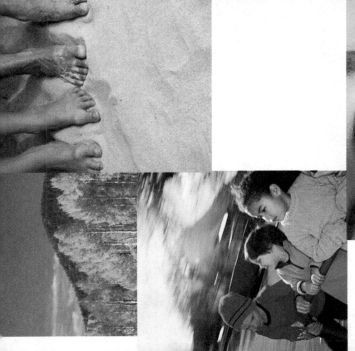

CONTENTS continued

Introduction

To the Student

The mind works like a video recorder, capturing images of our experiences every waking moment. It not only captures the daily images of personal experiences, but also records visual data from films, television shows, DVDs, advertisements, magazines, newspapers, signs, and music videos. We live an image-shaped existence.

Writers, like artists, take this image experience one step further: they draw on their images to create art. For the writer, this means using grammatical structures like brushstrokes of paint to create the reality they see and imagine.

This activities book is designed to show you how you can capture and create powerful images of your own by learning the grammatical painting techniques of outstanding authors.

Enjoy,
Harry Noden

Dedication

To my wife Jan, whose art inspired Image Grammar,
And whose intellect guided the editing

Selected Image Grammar Strategies:

Painting Brush Strokes

Learning to paint dynamic images is the work of the artist and the writer. Both must learn to use all of their senses to experience the world around them. Both must learn to observe specific details like the wrinkles in an old man's brow or the streaks of orange and red against black tree limbs in a fall sunset. The only difference is that the artist uses paint to capture images; the writer uses words.

The activities in this book are designed to show you how to paint with words. Each activity in this section illustrates a writer's technique—a strategy that is part of the writer's painting repertoire. Follow the instructions and learn how professional authors paint their worlds with words. We begin with five basic brush strokes that open doorways to what the writer sees and imagines.

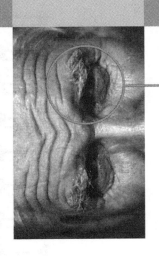

The Five Basic Brush Strokes

Use this page for reference as you learn to add brush strokes to your writing.

Core Sentence: The car went into the parking lot.

1. Adding an Absolute Brush Stroke

Engine smoking, gears grinding, the car went into the parking lot.

2. Adding an Appositive Brush Stroke

The car **, a 1936 Ford,** went into the parking lot.

3. Adding a Participle Brush Stroke

Sliding on the loose gravel, the car went into the parking lot.

4. Adding an Adjectives-Out-of-Order Brush Stroke

The car **, dented and rusty,** went into the parking lot.

5. Adding an Active Verb

The car **chugged** into the parking lot.

Absolute Brush Strokes

Imagine that you have written this sentence: "The car went into the parking lot." To strengthen this image, we are going to add a brush stroke called an **absolute**. It consists of a noun and an *-ing* word. Usually, you can add one or two absolute brush strokes to the beginning or end of a sentence. But if you add three, or if you drop these into the middle of a sentence, they lose some of their power. Here are a few examples that show absolutes used effectively.

Engine smoking, gears grinding,
the car went into the parking lot.

The car went into the parking lot, **wheels squeaking, bumper dragging.**

Directions for Activity 1

Examine the image below and follow these two steps: (1) Create a simple sentence describing the image. (2) Paint two absolutes at the beginning or end of your sentence. Write your description in the space provided on the next page.

Before you write, zoom in close with your visual and imaginative eye. Look at the surfer's arms, legs, and body posture. Imagine what he feels, how his mind is calculating, what he sees.

TIP Writers sometimes make a common error with absolutes by adding a distant image rather than one focused in the zoom lens. For example, if you created a core sentence beginning with "The surfer . . ." then added "Eagle flying off in the distance, the surfer . . ." the image of the eagle doesn't connect with the surfer. It wouldn't be seen in a close-up image. For maximum power with an absolute, zoom in on close-up details—the arms, legs, face, body, and mind of the surfer.

ACTIVITY 1 Paint with Absolute Brush Strokes

Description 1 (The Surfer)

1 _____

_____

Description 2

Using a magazine image, an Internet image, or an image from a book, create a second example of a sentence with two absolute brush strokes. Be sure to place them at the beginning or end of the sentence.

2 _____

_____

_____

Description 3

Watch an action scene from either a movie or from a sporting event on television. Write one sentence using two absolutes to describe a film character or an athlete.

3 _____

_____

Description 4

Picture a nature scene in your mind. Imagine the sensory details—the sounds, the smells, the feel of items you touch. Using two absolute brush strokes, write a sentence describing what you imagine.

4 _____

_____

Appositive Brush Strokes

Painting with an **appositive** brush stroke is like capturing the same subject with images from two different perspectives. After a noun (or noun phrase) in a basic sentence, you can add another noun, set it off with commas, and paint a second image in the mind of your reader. For example, let's begin with

our core sentence, "The car went into the parking lot." Suppose you want to add a second image to the word *car.* You can zoom in with a pair of commas after *car* and insert a second image, a noun that describes the car in a more specific way:

The car **, a 1936 Ford,** went into the parking lot.

Directions for Activity 2

For Description 1 on the facing page, follow these two steps: (1) Examine the image of the soldier and create a basic sentence about him (The soldier . . .). (2) Then zoom in with commas after the word *soldier* and consider some of the nouns that might be used as a second label for *soldier.* For example, he might be called a new recruit, a veteran, a father, a marine, or a renegade. Select a noun and build an appositive phrase by describing the noun with one or two descriptive words. For example, you might follow the word *soldier* with something like "the soldier, a tired marine clutching his M16A2 assault rifle, . . ."

ACTIVITY 2 Paint with Appositive Brush Strokes

Description 1 (The Soldier)

1 _____
_____
_____

Description 2

Locate an image of a face in a magazine or online and write one sentence describing the face with an appositive.

2 _____
_____
_____

Description 3

Think of an interesting place that you saw on television or in an advertisement. Picture the scene and write a sentence or two describing what you saw, using one appositive brush stroke in the description.

3 _____
_____
_____

Participle Brush Strokes

The next painting technique, a **participle** brush stroke, is similar to the absolute, but without the noun. It can be defined as an -*ing* word (or an -*ing* phrase) tagged onto the beginning or end of a sentence. Here is an example added to our sentence about the car.

Sliding on the loose gravel, the car went into the parking lot.

With participle brush strokes, you can either use one participial phrase as above or three single participles such as

Bouncing, *clanking*, *rattling*, the car went into the parking lot.

Directions for Activity 3

Study this image of a python for details and follow two steps: (1) Create a simple sentence describing the image. (2) Paint the image with either one participial phrase or three one-word participles at the beginning or end of your sentence. Write your sentence at the top of the following page.

Period

Name

ACTIVITY 3 Paint with Participle Brush Strokes

Description 1 (The Python)

1

_____

_____

Description 2

If the participle brush stroke you used in the description above was a long participial phrase, try painting the same image with three short participles. If you used three short participles, try one long participial phrase.

2

_____

_____

Description 3

Think of a dramatic event you observed or were in: an athletic event, a car crash, an argument, or for example. Describe the event in a sentence that includes a participle brush stroke.

3

_____

_____

Description 4

Think of an action scene in a movie or television show that you recently watched. Use a participle brush stroke in a sentence that captures a snapshot of that scene.

4

_____

_____

9

Adjectives Out-of-Order

Imagine that you are trying to teach someone how to write more descriptively and you examine a sentence the person has written that reads: The horse ran across the field. You say, "Add more description."

"O.K.," the person replies, and writes this sentence: The large, white, muscular horse ran across the field.

The writer has added adjectives, but stringing them in a row causes them to lose their effect. So, how do professional authors avoid this power loss and still find a way to pack in a string of adjectives when an image needs enhancing? They use a technique called **adjectives out-of-order,** in which two consecutive adjectives are positioned after the noun.

For example, rather than writing, "The **old, dented, rusty** car went into the parking lot," a professional author might write:

The **old** car, **dented and rusty,** went into the parking lot.

The professional example spotlights two of the adjectives, giving them more power and a sophisticated feel.

Examine the image of a baby leopard on the left and follow the directions for Description 1 on the facing page.

ACTIVITY 4 — Paint with Adjectives Out-of-Order

Description 1 (The Leopard)

Brainstorm a list of six adjectives that you might place in this sentence:

The _____ baby leopard listened to his father's commanding roar.

Next, eliminate those adjectives that writers call "image blanks." An image blank is an adjective that doesn't create a picture in your mind. For example, the adjectives *neat, beautiful, fascinating,* and *horrible* label how you feel, but they don't paint an image. By contrast, image adjectives leave a picture in your mind, like the words *red, tiny, furry, narrow, toothless,* and *sharp.* Finally, select from your list of adjectives three that best describe the baby leopard and fill in the sentence.

Description 2

Rewrite the following sentence using the adjectives out-of-order pattern:

His soiled, wrinkled, calloused hands portrayed a life of hard labor.

Description 3

Fill in the blanks with adjectives that create a visual image.

1 _____ _____ _____

The _____ baby leopard, _____

and _____, listened to his father's commanding roar.

2 _____

_____

_____

3 The _____ jogger, _____

_____, slowed from a fast sprint to a slow walk.

Action Verb Brush Strokes

How important is the use of action verbs? Jon Franklin, two-time Pulitzer Prize winner, says:

"Nothing is as critical as the use of action verbs.

This is absolutely—utterly, completely, with **shrieking boldface and CAPITAL LETTERS**—*CENTRAL to good writing."*

Picture the following image in your mind:

"The road was on the left side of the barn."

Notice how the image in your mind is a still photograph with no action. **Being verbs**—*is, was, were, are, am,* and other forms of the verb *to be*—freeze the image. Now, watch what happens to the image when the verb is changed:

"The road CUrled around the left side of the barn."

The image literally moves in your mind like a motion picture. This is the difference between *being* verbs and action verbs. Often, this brush stroke is added during the process of revision. A common problem with amateur writing is the overuse of *being* verbs. You should be able to eliminate somewhere between 50 and 70 percent of these verbs as you revise. Try this process of revision with a passage from Robert Louis Stevenson's *Treasure Island* on the facing page.

ACTIVITY 5 Paint with Action Verb Brush Strokes

Imagine that you are the author of *Treasure Island* and below is your rough draft. As you examine it, you realize that it is loaded with ineffective *being* verbs (*is*, *was*, *were*, *are*, and other forms of the verb *to be*) that slow down the pace. Rewrite the draft eliminating as many of the *being* verbs as you can by replacing them with brush strokes or action verbs. For example, you can combine sentences like "The dog sat under a tree. He was scratching his neck." Simply eliminate the *being* verb and create a participle: "The dog sat under a tree, scratching his neck."

Treasure Island Rough Draft with *Being* Verbs Added

I remember him as if it were yesterday. He was a tall, strong, heavy, nut-brown man. What was noticeable was his jet black pigtail and his soiled blue coat. He had a handspike. His hands were rugged and scarred with black broken nails, and there was a cut across one cheek of a dirty, livid white.

Rewrite of the Rough Draft from *Treasure Island*

_____

_____

_____

_____

_____

_____

The Artist's Brush Stroke Palette

The artist/writer builds images from a variety of palettes. One of the most powerful is the Artist's Brush Stroke Palette. Look at the image of the palette on the right and then examine the sample paragraph at the bottom of this page and the one on page 15. As you read, imagine that you are watching a famous author dip a brush into these five grammatical structures to paint word images.

In the paragraph below, notice how Ray Bradbury combines brush strokes in his short story, "The Sound of Thunder." To help you envision how Bradbury's mind works, each brush stroke is color-coded to match the palette. As you can see, the power of each individual brush stroke multiplies when it is combined with others.

And the head itself, a ton of sculptured stone, lifted easily upon the sky. Its mouth gaped, exposing a fence of teeth like daggers. **Its eyes rolled, ostrich eggs, empty of all expression save hunger. It** closed **its mouth in a death grin. It ran,** its pelvic bones crushing aside trees and bushes, its taloned feet clawing damp earth, leaving prints six inches deep wherever it settled its weight.

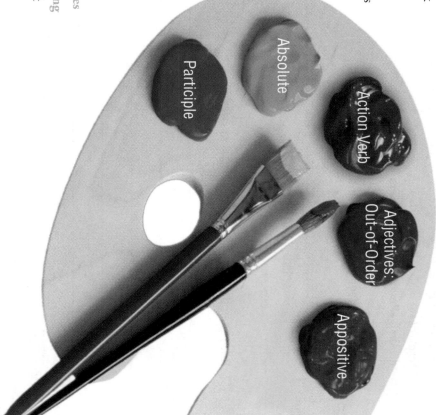

Participle

Absolute

Action Verb

Adjectives: Out-of-Order

Appositive

You can create a similar but less complicated paragraph than Bradbury's by combining the five basic brush strokes, using just one example of each. Here is a sample describing a lioness and her cubs:

The lioness, a new mother, yawned with a soft moaning roar. Twitching her whiskered nose, she squinted in the misty morning fog. Eyes telescoping the grassy plain, nostrils sniffing the wind, she tested each detail of the dawn before waking the rest of her cubs.

Directions for Activity 6

Now try describing one of the two images below using all five brush strokes. For Activity 6 on the facing page, create a four- or five-sentence paragraph. Use all five brush strokes, but don't use more than two strokes in a sentence. When you are finished, label each brush stroke in the margin.

As you write, be sure that most of your verbs are active and that they give movement to the action you are describing. *Being* verbs are sometimes needed for definitions and other functions, but nonprofessional writers use far too many, destroying the power of their images.

ACTIVITY 6

Use an Artist's Brush Stroke Palette

_____

_____

_____

_____

_____

_____

_____

_____

_____

_____

_____

_____

_____

_____

_____

See the following page for information on how your paragraph will be evaluated.

Name _____ Period _____

Rubric for the Brush Stroke Paragraph

Teachers often work with rubrics. Rubrics are key ideas that guide teachers when they evaluate assignments. To help you get a higher grade on this assignment, review the brush stroke rubric below. For each brush stroke that you accurately create and label, you will earn 10 points. Check your paragraph to be sure it contains one example of each of the five required brush strokes.

Each brush stroke used in your paragraph will be worth 10 points. Be sure to label each technique in the margin and draw an arrow to the example.

Absolute _____

Appositive _____

Adjectives Out-of-Order _____

Participle _____

Action Verbs _____

Total Points Earned = _____

Grade = _____

Teacher Comments

Paint a Favorite Image

From magazines you have at home or discards from the school or public library, locate two images that you especially enjoy—images that are no smaller than a half page of typing paper. Create a paragraph using brush strokes as you did for Activity 6.

Choose the image you want to write about and attach it to the paragraph you create. Turn in your second picture to help start a classroom collection of images for writing.

TIP If you have access to the Internet, go to Google http://www. google.com/, enter an image category (cars, football, dance, etc.), and click on "images." You will find hundreds that you can use for writing. Select one that you think would work well for this activity.

_____

_____

_____

_____

_____

_____

_____

_____

_____

_____

_____

Vocabulary Mind Melds

Imagine that you could magically step into the mind of Sue Grafton or Jack London and walk around examining the words and phrases they use to paint powerful images. Well, you can! Collecting palette samples helps you do just that. Palette samples are collections of words and phrases that authors have used to create their images.

Examine the palette samples on pages 21, 22, 24, and 25 collected from the work of mystery novelist Sue Grafton and adventure writer Jack London.

Directions for Activity 8

A mind meld is an old *Star Trek* term that the character Spock uses to describe his ability to travel into the mind of another person and read their thoughts. In a sense, we are going to travel into the mind of Sue Grafton, examine samples of her vocabulary images, and borrow a few to create a short descriptive scene. Here are the steps to follow:

1. Your teacher will divide you into teams of five or six. As a team, your task will be to write one or two paragraphs describing a situation in which a man and a woman meet and disagree. First, you need to select two characters for your scene. Some possibilities might include a witness and a cross-examining lawyer, a salesperson and a customer, a Gypsy mind reader and a client, a police officer and a suspect, a principal and a student, or a musician and a local reporter. If none of these appeal to you, create your own combination. As your team considers possible characters, examine Grafton's vocabulary images on pages 21 and 22. Her words might influence your choices.

2. Next, your team will create a scene. Elect one person as the chairman of your team to help lead your group discussion and another person as a recorder to write down the group's ideas. Decide on what will happen in your scene and begin to develop it by brainstorming sentences. You may borrow up to 25 percent of your total number of words from Sue Grafton's image vocabulary. Circle these words on your final copy.

In addition to using words taken from Sue Grafton's image vocabulary, you can create original images with similar grammatical structures. For example, Grafton uses the phrases "fragrance of crushed spices" and "reaching out tentatively." You might create a similar, but original image by writing, "odor of sweaty gym socks" and "creeping out slowly." This type of imitation would not count as part of your 25 percent, since you are not using exact vocabulary words taken from the author.

Vocabulary Images of Sue Grafton's Women

keys jingling between her fingers like castanets

smiled fleetingly

Barely glancing

shaggy mane

high cheekbones

complexion fresh and clean

eyes darkly charcoaled

tear-streaked face

babbled

one eye

cocked

red cashmere sweater

sleeves pushed up

groping blindly

false lashes

scrawny

untidy tangle of auburn hair

makeup smeared frog lips

clutched

Fumbling in her handbag for a Kleenex

tantalizing whiff

FLICKED

shrugged

halfway down her neck

like someone chewing ice

Vocabulary Images of Sue Grafton's Men

bony face

sagging cheeks

flinging an arm across the back of the chair

BREATHING
HOARSE
AND
WHEEZY

BLEARY-EYED

STARE

scrawny

big,
dark eyes

slouched
in his seat

dense brow over drooping eyelids

attitude of arrogance

**padding in his
plaid sport coat**

mustache
trailing down
around his mouth

panted

hands
in his
pockets

shaggy corn-yellow hair

sauntering

winked

leisurely pace

laced his
hands across
his head

perfunctory smile

hair combed away from his face

**SNAPPED
HIS FINGERS**

thick brows

ruddy complexion

*fragrance of
crushed spices*

Name _____   Period _____

Mind Meld with Sue Grafton

Names of Group Members_____

Brainstorm on scratch paper; then choose someone to write your group passage on the lines below.

_____
_____
_____
_____
_____
_____
_____
_____
_____
_____
_____
_____
_____
_____
_____

Brush Strokes from the Mind of Jack London

Absolutes

HAIR
BRISTLING

blood
flowing
from
nose and
mouth
and ears

lips writhing
and snarling

mouth foaming

JAWS CLIPPING TOGETHER

**body flashing
forward**

ears

laid

back

Muscles writhing
and knotting like
live things under
his silky fur

eyes diabolically
gleaming

chest panting futilely

Appositives and Noun Phrases

warm wet tongue

a lawgiver,
a master
to be
obeyed

blood-shot
eyes

PERPETUAL
SNARL

malignant eye

ice that bent and
crackled under foot

An oath from
Perrault—the
resounding
impact of a
club upon a
body frame

slavered

fangs

Elmo, a huge St. Bernard

Action Verbs

growled menacingly

sprang
for his
throat

sniffed

whirled
over

shrieked

taunted him

wagged circled
his tail

choked him

crawled to his feet

flung throbbed

BRISTLED HIS
NECK-HAIR
AND SNARLED

Adverbs

ORDERLY   shrewdly
imperiously
obscurely   mercilessly
calmly   **furiously**
slyly   docilely   curiously
aimlessly   instinctively
appeasingly

Adverbs are -ly words that describe the verb. Most authors use them sparingly because they prefer a strong verb that communicates the idea in the adverb. For example, rather than writing, "He walked slowly into the room," a skilled author might write "He sauntered into the room." Yet, adverbs are sometimes needed when an image or idea can't be conveyed through the verb. Jack London used some interesting ones.

Adjectives Out-of-Order and Adjectives

swarthy
ruthless   sour and introspective
mushy   bloody
limp and draggled
calm and impartial
lean and gaunt with a battle-scarred face   **evil-looking**
fierce looking
ragged and unkempt
parched and **mangled**
swollen   furry

Participles

shivering yelping
snarling and growling
pulling   sinking his teeth into it
till his tendons cracked
surging and wrestling
with it
snapping like a demon
BRISTLING
screaming with agony beneath the bristling mass of bodies   gasping painfully for air
sobbing for breath

ACTIVITY 9 A Mind Meld with Jack London

Imagine that you are writing the opening paragraph for an adventure story about a female German shepherd protecting her puppies from a starving mountain lion that is searching for food. Choose 25 percent or less of your brush stroke images from the Jack London palette samples on pages 24 and 25 and mix them with images of your own to create an exciting introduction.

As you did with the Sue Grafton activity, try to let London's words act as a catalyst for your own images. For example, London uses the phrases "lips writhing and snarling" and "eyes diabolically gleaming." You might create similar but original images by writing, "teeth snapping and clenching," and "eyes quickly surveying."

_____

_____

_____

_____

_____

_____

_____

_____

_____

_____

_____

_____

_____

_____

Create a Sketchbook

Artists often keep sketchbooks—spiral bound pages that capture the artist's images of both finished and unfinished works. In this activity we are going to imitate the artist by creating and collecting a variety of *written* images.

Your sketchbook will be a two-pocket folder to be used along with this activities book. One pocket of the folder will hold **Original Images,** those that you have written. These will include a wide variety of subjects ranging from writing completed in class to sketches created while watching sporting, musical, or entertainment events. The other pocket will be for **Found Images.** Found Images are those written by well-known authors. They are short passages—sentences, paragraphs, excerpts of poems—not complete works.

First Original Image for Your Sketchbook

For the first entry in your sketchbook, create a one-page description of an action scene. The action can come from a film, a sporting event, a concert, or even your imagination. As you write the scene, try to include a variety of brush strokes. Give your description a title, put it in your sketchbook, and list it on your **Record of Original Descriptions,** which is found on the following page. Any original description you put

in the sketchbook should be recorded on this list. Note that the Record has a column for Points Earned. Your teacher will determine the point value for each original description that is assigned, and explain how your work will be evaluated.

First Found Image for Your Sketchbook

Your next assignment will be to locate and copy a short passage that you found especially powerful. Examples can come from almost any written source including novels, magazines, short stories, poems, newspaper articles, and song lyrics. Be prepared to explain why you selected this passage and any others you collect in your sketchbook. For this first entry, don't be concerned about locating passages with brush strokes. Just find sample passages that you like. Later, after you have worked with brush strokes for a while, you can locate brush stroke examples in the works you are reading.

On your **Record of Found Paragraph Images,** page 29, note the author's name, the title of the work, and the page number where you found the image.

Name _____ Period _____

ACTIVITY 10 *Create a Sketchbook*

Record of Original Descriptions

Title of Description   **Points Earned**   **Teacher's Initials**

1. _____   _____   _____

2. _____   _____   _____

3. _____   _____   _____

4. _____   _____   _____

5. _____   _____   _____

6. _____   _____   _____

7. _____   _____   _____

8. _____   _____   _____

9. _____   _____   _____

10. _____   _____   _____

Record of Found Paragraph Images

Copy your found images below. Then identify the author, title of the source, and page number for each. Duplicate this page if you need room for additional entries.

1. Found Image

Author _____

Title _____ Page _____

2. Found Image

Author _____

Title _____ Page _____

3. Found Image

Author _____

Title _____ Page _____

4. Found Image

Author _____

Title _____ Page _____

Name _____ Period _____

ACTIVITY 11

ACTIVITY 11 Record of Found Phrase and Sentence Images

To build your image vocabulary and start you seeing and thinking like a professional, collect short images of phrases and sentences to store in your sketchbook. Collect them at first by categories: action images, character images, and setting images. Then expand your collection by brush stroke categories as in the Jack London collection on pages 24 and 25.

Found Action Images

Found Character Images

Found Setting Images

Name _____   Period _____

ACTIVITY 11 *continued*

Once you have collected a number of phrases and sentences, expand your image collection by locating samples of brush strokes and listing them in the categories below.

Absolutes

Appositives

Participles

Adjectives Out-of-Order

Action Verbs

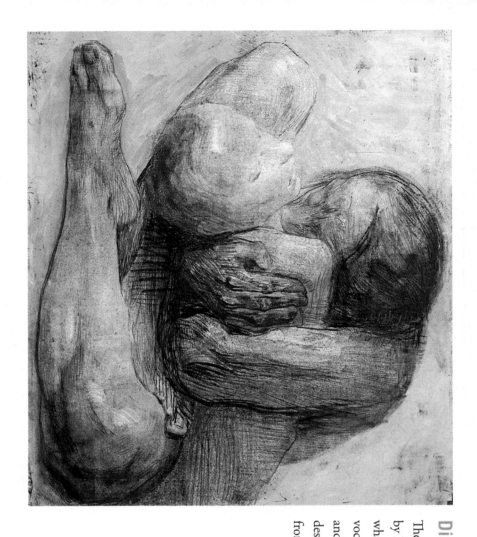

Directions for Activity 12

The etching at the left is entitled *Woman with Dead Child* by Kathe Kollwitz. Write a description of what you see and what you imagine as you examine this piece. Use your image vocabulary and brush strokes to make your writing as powerful and moving as the artwork itself. To help you create your description, you may borrow up to 20 percent of your phrases from the found images you recorded on pages 30 and 31.

Name _____

ACTIVITY 12 Use Your Found Images

Advanced Brush Strokes

This section of the activities book is not designed to cover all of the complex constructions authors use but simply to introduce you to a few examples of how writers combine and expand the basic brush strokes. Using what you have already learned, you can experiment with these advanced brush strokes by combining them. Here are a few examples to get you started.

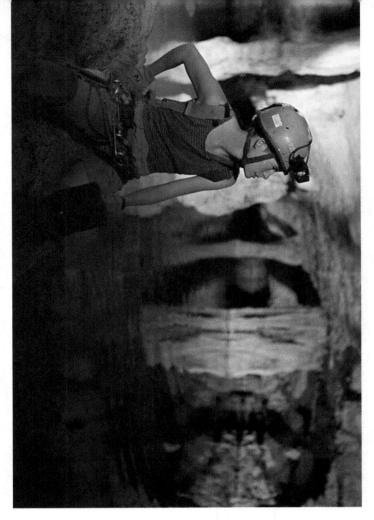

A Participle Series

Brush strokes in a series is one of the easier advanced concepts. It is simply a repetition of a single brush stroke. For example, look at this sentence.

The headlight on the bike bounced up and down, **jerking the shadows on the terrain ahead, making it difficult to see what was coming.**

—Michael Crichton, *Prey*

Added to the core sentence are two participial phrases, one beginning with the word *jerking*, the other with the word *making*.

34

ACTIVITY 13 Paint with a Series of Participles

1. Try to imitate a participle series using the photograph on page 34. First, examine the image, then use this core sentence to set the scene:

> The spotlight on her miner's helmet illuminated the cave.

Picture the images that this explorer might see and add two -*ing* phrases. A few participles that could work well with this type of image include *revealing, showing, uncovering, spotlighting, exposing, divulging,* and *unmasking.*

1 _____

_____

_____

2. Now, rework the sentence using different participles.

2 _____

_____

_____

3. Finally, write an original sentence using a participle series.

3 _____

_____

_____

Brush Stroke Combinations

Combinations of different brush strokes are another category of the writer's painting techniques. They are a little more difficult to paint, but they create dynamic images when used.

A Participle/Absolute Combination

A participle/absolute combination is one of the more frequent writing techniques and is easy to use if you have mastered each as a single brush stroke. Notice how John Steinbeck uses this combination:

> A little bit ahead he saw the high-domed shell of a land turtle, **crawling slowly along through the dust,** its legs working stiffly and jerkily.
>
> —John Steinbeck, *The Grapes of Wrath*

His core sentence is followed with the participle phrase "**crawling slowly along through the dust,**" and then he adds an absolute phrase, "**its legs working stiffly and jerkily.**" In the next activity, imitate Steinbeck's advanced brush stroke.

Directions for Activity 14

Examine the details in the painting on the facing page by N. C. Wyeth.

Imagine that you are on an island watching these pirates storm a makeshift fort, a fort protected by a small band of British seamen. Visualize the action of the attackers; imagine the sounds; zoom in on the details. Then select one of the pirates and describe him in a sentence using an absolute/participle combination. Use John Steinbeck's sentence as a model. Don't forget to use your imaginative eye as well as your visual eye.

ACTIVITY 14   Paint a Participle/Absolute Combination

For this activity, start with the following clause and add a participle and an absolute in the spaces provided.

At the head of the charging band of pirates, I spotted Captain Kidd, ...

(participle) _____

_____

_____

_____

_____

(absolute) _____

_____

_____

_____

Name _____

Period _____

Experiment with Selected Techniques

As a final brush stroke assignment, write a paragraph describing
the image on the left. Experiment with a few of the techniques
you have learned, mixing some basic brush strokes with one or
two of the more advanced constructions.

_____

_____

_____

_____

_____

_____

_____

_____

_____

_____

_____

_____

_____

_____

The Musical Rhythms of Language

In the world of music, words and phrases cascade across our minds when we listen to song lyrics. Lyrics are so interwoven with the musical rhythms that it is almost impossible to repeat a lyric without singing its companion melody.

In the world of fiction, poetry, and nonfiction, a different type of musical rhythm flows through our subconscious—a subtle rhythm, almost undetectable, flowing like soft drumbeats of words and phrases. You can hear these rhythms in almost every genre: advertisements, film scripts, political speeches, popular science books, and best-selling novels.

Rhythms in Parallel Structures

Read the following passages and see if you can feel the rhythm indicated in boldface type. The rhythm is developed through the repetition of words and phrases. This repetition is referred to as **parallelism**—the use of parallel structures.

From a Pulitzer Prize-winning autobiography

Never shall I forget that smoke. Never shall I forget the little faces of the children, whose bodies I saw turned into wreaths of smoke beneath a silent blue sky. **Never shall I forget those flames which** consumed my faith forever. **Never shall I forget that nocturnal silence which** deprived me, for all eternity, of the desire to live. **Never shall I forget those moments which** murdered **my God** and **my soul** and turned **my dreams** to dust. **Never shall I forget these things**, even if I am condemned to live as long as God Himself. **Never.**

—Elie Wiesel, *Night*

From a television advertisement

In his nightmares he can see them. In his mind he can hear them. In his soul he can feel them. Now in earth's darkest hour, **he must fight them** again. But this time, they must travel to the past to save our future.

—advertisement for the film *First Contact*

From a magazine advertisement

When you give blood
you give **another birthday,
another anniversary,
another day at the beach,
another night under the stars,
another talk with a friend,
another laugh,
another hug,
another chance.**

Please give blood.

—advertisement for the American Red Cross

Directions for Activity 1

Our language is filled with music, and the best way to feel this music is to imitate passages that create strong melodies. Try the following exercise.

Step 1 Select a Debatable Topic

After your teacher has divided you into several groups, select a debatable topic from the options below. Naturally there will be different views among your group members, so you will need to either find a topic your group can agree on or compromise and select a viewpoint that the majority of the group supports. Keep in mind that although you are arguing a position, the purpose of this activity is to feel the rhythm, not debate the topic. So don't feel concerned if you find yourself creating arguments that support a view with which you disagree.

Here are some choices:

Should human cloning be banned?

Should animals have rights?

Should music lyrics be censored?

Should all Americans be required to carry an identity card?

Should high school athletes be required to take drug tests?

Should abortion be outlawed?

Should formal prayer in schools be encouraged?

Should United States immigrants be required to speak English?

Should students be required to wear school uniforms?

Should proficiency tests be abandoned?

Should boxing be banned?

Should we abolish the death penalty?

Should the Ten Commandments be displayed in schools?

Should the U.S. have invaded Iraq?

Should all schools be private and run for profit?

Should we work to halt global warming?

Should we establish free health care for all Americans?

Should laws be passed to limit gun ownership?

Should immoral films, video games, and books be banned?

Step 2 Examine a Rhythmic Pattern

After you have selected a topic, examine the following passage from a film advertisement. This will be the model for your imitation.

Between what can be seen and what can be feared, between what lives and what never dies, between the light of truth and the darkness of evil lies the future of terror.

—television advertisement for *Lord of Illusions*

Step 3 Fill in the Blanks

As a team, fill in the blanks in the template on the following page. Insert your own images and ideas. Do not explicitly reveal your topic until the last phrase: "lies the blank of blank." For example, if your topic is cloning and you are opposed to it, you might end with "lies the problem with cloning."

Name _____ Period _____

Feel the Rhythm

Group Number _____

Between what _____ and what

_____ and what _____, between what

_____ of _____, between the

_____ of _____ and the _____ of

_____, lies the _____ of _____.

Bonus Option: Go online to http://www.americanrhetoric.com/ or search your library collection for an interesting speech. Locate one or two rhythmic lines in the speech and copy those lines here:

_____

_____

_____

_____

_____

_____

_____

_____

Types of Parallel Structures

The musical rhythms of language can be created with a variety of grammatical forms, but **parallel structures** are the most common. Writers rely on three types of parallel structures—(1) literal repetitions, (2) grammatical repetitions, and (3) a combination of literal and grammatical repetitions.

Literal Repetition

This is the easiest technique to both recognize and create. It simply involves a repetition of the same word or phrase. For example, notice the lyrical repetition in this excerpt from the film *Wall Street*. The central character, Gordon Gekko (played by Michael Douglas), is addressing a shareholders' meeting of a corporation he is about to strip of its assets. Notice how the screenwriters (Oliver Stone and Stanley Weiser) emphasize the word "greed" to drive home Gekko's materialistic philosophy.

The point is, ladies and gentlemen, that **greed**, for lack of a better word, is good. **Greed** is right. **Greed** works. **Greed** clarifies, cuts through and captures the essence of the evolutionary spirit. **Greed**, in all of its forms—**greed** for life, for money, for love, knowledge—has marked the upward surge of mankind.

A literal repetition can also introduce a collection of items that do not repeat a defined grammatical structure. Here is an example from Billy Joel's commencement speech to the graduates of Fairfield University in May of 1991. In this speech he imagines what it might be like if he could travel back in time 20 years earlier and meet himself at age 21.

What would I think of him? **Would I** find him to be naive, arrogant, simplistic, crude, noble, hopelessly idealistic? Perhaps all of these things. But more important, **what would he** think of me? **Have I** fulfilled his dream? **Have I** created the kind of music he would have wanted to have written? **Have I** compromised any of his ideals? **Have I** broken any of the promises I made to him? **Have I** lost the desire to be the best he could be? **Would he** be disappointed in me? **Would he** even like me?

P# Pure Grammatical Repetition

Pure grammatical repetition occurs when a writer's words pound a drumbeat without any literal repetitions. These rhythms are hard to recognize since there is no visual clue—no repeated word or phrase—that signals the rhythm. For example, listen for the grammatical rhythm in this sentence:

Over the river and **through the woods, to grandmother's house,** we go.

Three prepositional phrases set up the rhythm of grammatical repetition, but there are no literal repetitions.

Shakespeare used grammatical repetition frequently in both his poems and plays. Before you read some lines from one of his poems, try sounding the rhythmic de Dah pattern. Note that the Dah receives the emphasis and the de Dum sets up a rhyme that enhances the musical quality. This rhythm, popular with poets in Shakespeare's time, is called *iambic pentameter*. Sound out the de Dah quatrain (a quatrain is a four-line stanza) below.

> de DAH de DAH de DAH de DAH de DAH,
> de DAH de DAH de DAH de DAH de DUM;
> de DAH de DAH, de DAH de DAH, de DAH
> de DAH, de DAH de DAH de DAH, de DUM.

Now see how Shakespeare used this rhythm in Sonnet 73. In the following stanza, the unstressed words or syllables are indicated by a caret (^) and the stressed beats are indicated with a slash mark (/).

Quatrain from Shakespeare's Sonnet 73

```
  ^    /    ^    /    ^   /    ^   /   ^    /
That time  of year  thou mayst  in me  be hold

  ^     /     ^    /     ^    /    ^    /   ^   /
When yel  low leaves,  or none,  or few,  do hang

 ^   /     ^      /      ^      /     ^     /    ^    /
Up on   those boughs  which shake  a gainst  the cold,

 ^    /    ^     /      ^    /     ^    /     ^    /
Bare ru   ind choirs,  where late  the sweet  birds sang.
```

Combined Literal and Grammatical Repetition

Combining literal and grammatical repetition is the most common form of parallel structure. Writers create a profound tone by combining an obvious literal repetition with a repetitive grammatical structure. Here are a few examples:

The world is changed. **I feel it in the water. I feel it in the earth. I smell it in the air.**

—From the film script *Fellowship of the Rings*

Notice how the screenwriter used a literal repetition for the words "I feel it," and then added different endings with the same grammatical structure with "in the water," "in the earth," and "in the air." In the last sentence, the verb *smell* replaces "feel" but the drumbeat is the same.

Here is another example. In this advertisement, the writer emphasized grammatical repetitions in the first two sentences and then combined a literal repetition with a grammatical repetition in the third, fourth, and fifth sentences.

Ambition inspired his journey. Nature changed his destiny. One survivor. One island. One warrior. Two men against all odds.

—From an advertisement for the film *Robinson Crusoe*

Here is another literal-grammatical combination from Martin Luther King, Jr.'s, classic speech "I Have a Dream."

With this faith, we will be able to hew out of the **mountain of despair a stone of hope. With this faith, we will be able to** transform the **jangling discords of our nation** into a **beautiful symphony of brotherhood. With this faith, we will be able to work together, to pray together, to struggle together, to go to jail together, to stand up for freedom together,** knowing that we will be free one day.

Rod Serling's *Twilight Zone*

Rod Serling, the creator of the old *Twilight Zone* television series, was a master of musical word rhythms. In the next activity you are going to imitate his *Twilight Zone* introduction. But first, you will need to select one of these topics:

The Sports Zone	The Nature Zone
The Music Zone	The Human Trait Zone
The Political Zone	The Crime Zone
The School Zone	The Job Zone

Or you may want to use more specific categories such as

The Steelers Zone	The Eagle Zone	
The Broncos Zone	The Gator Zone	
The Skateboard Zone	The Forest Zone	
The Martial Arts Zone	The Everest Zone	
The Rap Zone	The Desert Zone	
The Bluegrass Zone	The Love Zone	
The Rock Zone	The Hate Zone	
The Math Zone	The Friendship Zone	
The English Zone	The Car Wash Zone	
The Cafeteria Zone	The Burger Cook Zone	
The Republican / Democratic Zone		

Once you have selected a topic, review Rod Serling's introduction:

There is a fifth dimension beyond that which is known to man. It is a dimension as vast as space and as timeless as infinity. It is the middle ground between light and shadow, between science and superstition, and it lies between the pit of man's fears, and the summit of his knowledge. This is the dimension of imagination. It is an area which we call . . . THE TWILIGHT ZONE.

ACTIVITY 2

Feel the Rhythms of the *Twilight Zone*

Your task is to fill in the template below with images and ideas that describe the type of zone you selected.

The _____ Zone

There is a fifth dimension beyond that which is known to man. It is a dimension as

_____ and as _____. It is the _____

_____ between _____ and _____, between

_____, and it lies between the _____ of _____, and

the _____ of his/her _____. This is the dimension of _____. It is an

area which we call . . .THE _____ ZONE.

Rhythms Using Prepositions

Musical rhythms come in all kinds of grammatical shapes, but many are constructed with prepositions, relative pronouns, and subordinate conjunctions, three types of words that function like mortar holding together image bricks.

Prepositions

Let's examine each of these connecting words in turn. Here is a list of the prepositions that are most often used to create language rhythms:

about	before	from	over
above	below	in	through
across	beneath	into	to
after	beside	like	toward
against	between	near	under
along	beyond	of	underneath
amid	by	on	until
around	down	onto	with
at	for	outside	without

Notice how prepositional phrases are used in the sentence below to develop a powerful rhythm.

> The cosmos is rich beyond measure—**in elegant facts, in exquisite interrelationships, in the subtle machinery of awe.**

> —*Carl Sagan, Cosmos*

The preposition *in* connects the beat. Similarly, Martin Luther King, Jr., uses the preposition *from* to build intensity in his "I Have a Dream" speech:

> And so let freedom ring **from** the prodigious hilltops of New Hampshire. Let freedom ring **from** the mighty mountains of New York. Let freedom ring **from** the heightening Alleghenies of Pennsylvania. Let freedom ring **from** the snow-capped Rockies of Colorado. Let freedom ring **from** the curvaceous slopes of California.

King also uses literal repetition with the phrase "let freedom ring" to enhance the rhythmic power even further.

ACTIVITY 3 Create a Prepositional Phrase Pattern

Step 1

Think about some activity you have experienced such as working on a hobby, playing a sport, performing music, or creating art. Review the Carl Sagan *Cosmos* passage on the previous page. Then use the template that follows to create a rhythmic passage describing your selected activity or experience.

Step 2

Now create a prepositional rhythm of your own. Think of an interesting place where you would like to be—a room, a park, a field, a shop, a river, a lake, a concert hall, a sports arena, etc. Then select three different prepositions from the list on page 48 and create a sentence with three prepositional phrases ending with words that identify your place. For example, "**Beyond** Raber's farm, **along** the High Ridge Woods, **near** a grove of red maple trees, lies a little-known trout stream."

1 _____ is rich beyond

measure—in _____ , in

_____ , in the

_____

of _____ .

2 _____ ,

_____ ,

_____ ,

lies _____ .

Rhythms Using Relative Pronouns and Subordinate Conjunctions

In addition to prepositions, subordinate conjunctions and relative pronouns also create rhythms. Just as with prepositions, certain subordinate conjunctions and relative pronouns create more effective rhythms than others. They are listed below.

Subordinate Conjunctions

after	even if	until	wherever
although	even though	whatever	whether
as	if	when	whichever
as if	since	whenever	while
because	so that	where	
before	unless	whereas	

Relative Pronouns

| that | who | whose |
| which | whoever | |

Similar to prepositions, both subordinate conjunctions and relative pronouns create musical rhythms when repeated. Listen to these two examples, the first constructed with the subordinate conjunction *when* and the second with the relative pronoun *who*.

When children learn to live without prejudice and greed, **when** nations resolve conflicts without bloodshed, **when** women take leadership roles in national governments, only then will the world have peace.

She was a woman **who** reached out to save the endangered mountain gorillas, **who** challenged the jungle warlords, **who**, in the end, gave her life protecting the animals she loved.

Repetitions of all kinds occur in both fiction and nonfiction. Here the repeated word *where* sets up a rhythm:

Near the banks of the Muscatatuck **where once the woods had stretched, dark row on row,** and **where the fox grapes and wold mint still flourished,** Jess Birdwell, an Irish Quaker, built his white clapboard house.

—Jessamyn West, *Friendly Persuasion*

Notice how the subordinate conjunction *if* sets up the rhythm in the following advertisement and enhances the clauses that begin with "How do you explain…"

If there are no UFOs, **if** ghosts really don't exist, **if** angels are only a myth, then **how do you explain** the traces? **How do you explain** the sounds? And most of all, **how do you explain** the sightings? Beyond imagination lies the truth.

—advertisement for the film *UFOs: Fact or Fiction?*

ACTIVITY 4   Create a Pattern with a Subordinate Conjunction

Examine the photograph of interlocking archways made of stone. Let your imagination wander, picturing what type of place this might be or might have been. Then use your imagined details to complete the rhythmic template that follows.

It was an exotic hideaway where _____

_____ where

_____

_____, and where _____

_____ .

Now try using the subordinate conjunction *if*.

If _____, if

_____, if

_____ .

then _____ .

ACTIVITY 5 *Create a Pattern with a Relative Pronoun*

Look at the photo of the London street artist below. A street artist creates art on sidewalks, on parking lots, on walkways— wherever there is cement. Often, street art is created with

pastels that dissolve with the first rainstorm. Imagine what this artist might have done that led him to this unusual profession and then complete the template that follows.

He was a street artist who _____

_____ , who

_____ , and who

_____ .

ACTIVITY 6 Create a "Good Old Days" Passage

Ask your (select one: mother, father, grandmother, grandfather, uncle, neighbor) in what year he or she was born. Use this date to examine the decade from the time your selected individual was 10 years old until he or she was 20. If possible, interview the person you plan to write about. Find out what life was like when he or she was your age.

Then complete your research using library materials, old family photos, and Web sites to locate some interesting information and images. Use the parallel structure model that follows to write your passage and write it as though you are a reporter doing a documentary.

Note: To locate Internet information, just type the decade you want to examine (1950s, 1960s, etc.) into a Google search and you will find a variety of sources.

The Good Old Days

Between 19_____ and 19_____, the early years when _____ (name of your subject) _____ was young, life was radically

different. **Those were the days when** _____

_____

_____

Those were the days when _____

_____ and _____

_____.

continued

ACTIVITY 6 continued

In those days families _____

_____

In those days teens _____ and _____

_____. They

idolized _____ like _____ , and

_____ like _____ who

_____ .

In those days life seemed less expensive. A _____ cost

_____ .

A _____ cost _____ . You could buy a _____

for _____ . Those were the days—days when _____

_____ , when _____

and when _____

_____ .

Those were the good old days for _____

_____ (Insert name such as "Uncle

Jed," or "Mother," or "my neighbor Mr. Weinstein").

Selected Details:

The Close-up Power of the Zoom Lens

Zoom for Close-ups of Specific Details

In an audiotape entitled *How to Write a Novel*, John Braine, a popular novelist in the 1950s, revealed an important secret that helped him write the best-selling novel *Room at the Top*:

The overall rule for writing is to keep it concrete, to avoid the abstract. This rule for writing good prose was lifted straight from Stuart Chase's *Tyranny of Words*. This has been the most important book of my life. If I have been able to make a living as a writer, it has been entirely due to reading Chase's book at a formative age.

The central concept in *Tyranny of Words*, the concept Braine valued above all others, is an idea called "Levels of Abstraction." **Levels of abstraction** refers to the way words can be classified based on how distant they are from specific images.

The Ladder of Abstraction

Economic Commodity

Creature

Farm Animal

Pig

Waddle

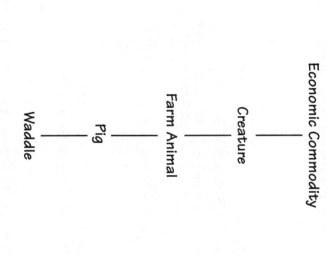

Imagine that you owned a pet pig named Waddle. For you, the word *Waddle* creates a very specific image. Waddle is the pig who waddles, the pig that snorts when his food arrives, the pig with long ears that swing down almost at eye level. These words provide you with a very detailed mental picture of the pig. This detailed level of language is called the lowest level of abstraction.

Now say that you ignore all those colorful and specific details that provided a vivid picture of Waddle and merely refer to him as a "pig." You are characterizing him with only a few general qualities that help to identify all pigs, but nothing more. If you refer to Waddle as a "farm animal," the specific image in your mind's eye becomes even more vague. Look at the diagram on the left and notice how your specific mental image of Waddle disappears as you move from the name "Waddle" up an imaginary ladder of abstraction to the more abstract words *creature* and *economic commodity*. Specific images, a primary tool of writers, are always found on the lowest level of abstraction.

When you reach the top step, and refer to Waddle as an "economic commodity," the specific images of Waddle vanish. This is why authors like Ezra Pound and Ernest Hemingway have urged young writers to avoid abstractions. Writing with abstractions is the equivalent of displaying blurred photographs of distant subjects. To get a sense of how language falls on various levels of abstraction, try the activity on the next two pages.

ACTIVITY 1 Sort the Levels

Unscramble each list on a ladder of abstraction, placing the word that is closest to an actual real world experience at the lowest level.

Word List 1

creature   dog   St. Bernard
animal   Cujo

_____ (highest level)

_____

_____

_____

_____ (lowest level)

Word List 2

public asset   book   *The Sherlock Holmes Reader*
novel   library material

_____ (highest level)

_____

_____

_____

_____ (lowest level)

continued

Name _____ Period _____

Word List 3

dessert   half-gallon of fudge ripple

ice cream   food   store inventory

_____ (highest level)

_____

_____

_____

_____ (lowest level)

Word List 4

Star Wars IV   sci-fi film   movie

George Lucas flick   entertainment

_____ (highest level)

_____

_____

_____

_____ (lowest level)

Word List 5

Create your own word list starting on the bottom rung with the name of a famous celebrity or well-known historical figure.

_____ (highest level)

_____

_____

_____

_____ (lowest level)

Name

Painting a Noun Collage with Specific Images

Authors rely on words that convey images by using specific details. Sometimes, when writers combine a collection of noun images—complete with adjectives and prepositional phrases—they create a "noun" collage. Much like an artist's collage, the noun collage combines fragments (collected images) into a unified whole. Here are a few examples:

Collage of a Setting

Seen in a Junk Yard. Dogs, chickens with few claws, brass fittings, T's elbow, rust everywhere, bales of metal 1800 lbs., plumbing fixtures, bathtubs, sinks, water pumps, wheels, Fordson tractor, acetylene lamps for tractors, sewing machine, bell on dinghy, box of bolts (No. 1), van, stove, auto stuff (No. 2), army trucks, cast iron body, hot dog stand, dinky engines, sprockets like watch parts, hinge all taken apart on building side, motorcycle radiators, George on the high army truck.

—F. Scott Fitzgerald, *The Great Gatsby*

Collage of a Character

The policeman leaned across the seat, opened the passenger door. He stared at the mud-crusted boots, the rumpled jeans ripped at the cuffs and patched on one thigh, the blue sweatshirt speckled with what looked like dry blood, the buckskin jacket. He lingered over the beard and the long hair.

—David Morrell, *First Blood*

Collage of Symbolic Objects (Indirect Characterization)

I could see the fuzzy sleeve of my father's green angora sweater poking out of one carton, and through the finger holes in the side of another, I could make out the cracked spines of his college chemistry texts. Stuffed into the spaces among the boxes and into odd nooks of the car's interior were my father's bicycle helmet, his clarinet case, his bust of Paul Morphy, his brass wall barometer, his shoeshine kit, his vaporizer, the Panama hat he liked to wear at the beach, the long plastic bedpan that had come home from the hospital with him after his deviated-septum operation and now held his razors and combs and the panoply of gleaming instruments he employed to trim the hair that grew from various features of his face. A grocery bag full of his shoe trees, his Morphy Junior Chess Championship Trophy he had won in 1953, his tie rack, his earmuffs, and one Earth shoe.

—Michael Chabon, "Werewolves in Their Youth"

Directions for Activity 2

Select either of the two images below or locate an image of your own and create a collage paragraph loaded with noun images. The writing of a collage paragraph is one of the few instances where authors use fragments for effect. In this rare instance, you may use fragments as well.

For this activity, you will need to use both your imaginative eye and visual eye. Think about a time when you were in a city during rush hour traffic or in a football stadium during a winning touchdown. Try to recall images of those sights, and begin collecting your nouns. Explore your memories for sounds, smells, sights, and sensory images of touch. Use the images below as a catalyst, letting the photos evoke memories of your actual experiences.

Name _____

ACTIVITY 2

Create a Noun Collage

Zooming and Layering

Zooming

The heart of writing, as you have learned, is the power of specific details—details described in images that we can visualize. But how do authors accomplish this? They zoom in on nouns and verbs, and then layer in supporting details with adjectives, prepositional phrases and brush strokes. For example, a writer might create the following sentence:

> The **boat went** through the waves on the **lake**. The **waves were** high and **came** down. The **storm made** our minds fearful.

To revise these sentences and make them more powerful, a skilled writer might begin by "zooming" in on nouns and verbs (in blue and red boldface above). The nouns—*boat, lake, waves,* and *storm*—are abstract. They don't provide a specific image. So the writer's task is to replace these nouns using a mental zoom lens. If we allow our imagination to create a close-up image, the boat might be a tanker, a sailboat, or a rowboat. With a zoom technique on nouns, writers have two options: they can zoom in and add an appositive brush stroke, or they can zoom in and replace the noun with a more specific noun.

Zooming in on verbs is a similar process. In the sample sentences, the verbs *went, were, came,* and *made* send blank images into the mind of the reader. So, a skilled writer zooms in and visualizes an action verb. For example, the word *went* might be replaced with a close-up image like *crashed, slammed,* or *plunged*. Consequently, a revised passage with the zoom technique would look something like this:

> The **rowboat plunged** into the waves on **Lake Erie**. **White caps crested** and then **cascaded**. The **rain and lightning rippled** our minds with fear.

Layering

Next, the writer might use a technique called *layering*. Layering means adding specific details using adjectives, prepositional phrases, and brush strokes. In conjunction with zooming in on nouns and verbs, layering enhances the images even more. On the next page (boldfaced and color coded) are the five types of layering techniques that can be used with any passage. Some suggested layering ideas for the passage above follow each category.

1. Participle Brush Strokes
swirling above the boat, dancing like the wings of vultures

2. Absolute Brush Strokes
hull groaning, oars creaking, water sloshing

3. Adjectives and/or Adjectives Out-of-Order
leaky, relentless, four-foot, rickety, tiny

4. Appositives
old wooden Acme Skiff

5. Prepositional Phrases
in the moonlight, into the five-foot waves, upon us

Layering after Zooming

Here you can see the final effect after layering has been added:

Hull groaning, the **leaky** rowboat, **an old wooden Acme Skiff,** plunged into the five-foot waves on Lake Erie. **Swirling above the boat, dancing like the wings of vultures,** white caps crested **in the moonlight** and then cascaded **upon us.** The relentless rain and lightning rippled our minds with fear.

TIP Test your adjectives to be sure they are on a low level of abstraction. Picture the adjective in your mind. Does it paint a detail or does it simply label with an abstract term. General adjectives like *beautiful, wonderful, loving, strange,* and so forth, are not visual. Use visual adjectives such as *furry, red,* and *wrinkled.*

ACTIVITY 3 Paint by Zooming and Layering

Revise each sentence in this activity by zooming and layering, using the procedure on the previous page as a model. Begin by zooming in on just the nouns and verbs marked with boldface and replacing them with specific examples. After completing each sentence by zooming, revise by layering.

Sentence 1

Revise with Zooming

The **creature went** into the **water** and **moved** past the **woman.**

1 _____

_____

_____

_____

Revise by Layering

Next, layer over your revised sentence above by adding two of the following: a participle brush stroke, an absolute brush stroke, two adjectives and/or adjectives out-of-order, and a prepositional phrase.

_____

_____

_____

_____

_____

continued

Zoom and layer Sentences 2 and 3 on a piece of scratch paper, then write a final version in the space provided. Keep in mind that layering needs to include only two of the five techniques.

Sentence 2

As you did with Sentence 1, zoom in on the nouns and verbs marked with boldface in Sentence 2 and replace them with specific examples.

With the **dog** close behind him, the **cat went** over the fence and **ran** up a **tree** to safety.

Next, layer over your revision of Sentence 2 by adding a combination of any two of the following: a participle brush stroke, an absolute brush stroke, adjectives and/or adjectives out-of-order, and a prepositional phrase.

2 _____

_____

_____

_____

Sentence 3

Create two sentences describing an event (sporting, musical, drama, etc.) that you experienced in the past year.

3 _____

_____

_____

_____

_____

Painting Bai Yun and Su Lin

Name _____ Period _____

At the left is a photo of Bai Yun and her baby girl Su Lin, who was born in the San Diego Zoo 21 weeks before the photo was taken. Write a short descriptive paragraph of the mother embracing her cub. Don't worry about zooming or layering with this rough draft. You can do that when you revise.

Rough Draft

_____
_____
_____
_____
_____
_____
_____
_____
_____
_____
_____

continued

ACTIVITY 4 continued

Now revise your description by zooming and layering with specific details. Use scratch paper for your initial changes and then copy your final draft below.

Final Draft

_____

_____

_____

_____

_____

_____

_____

_____

_____

_____

_____

_____

_____

For more details on Bai Yun and Su Lin, go to http://www.sandiegozoo.org/news/panda_news.html

Creating Humor with Specific Images

Specific images also create humor. Try eliminating all of the specific images in a comedian's monologue, and watch the humor evaporate. For example, look at Dave Barry's comment on the aging Rolling Stones, first with all specific images removed:

As I write these words, the remaining Stones are still out there on tour, still rockin' and rollin' and putting on an electrifying act.

Now look at Barry's original passage, which is loaded with specific images to create humor:

As I write these words, the remaining **non-deceased** Stones, **some of whom were born during the Hundred Years War**, are still out there on tour, still rockin and rollin' and putting on an electrifying act **that reaches its climax during "Satisfaction" when drummer Charlie Weaver hurls his dentures into the crowd.**

Similarly, David Letterman's Top Ten Lists are always examples of specific images that would have lost their impact as generalizations. For example, in his list of the "Top Ten Signs That Your Kid's School Is Too Crowded," Letterman could have made a general statement like, "Your child tells

you that there were too many people on the bus." But instead Letterman's writers created a specific image with "Your kid comes home happy saying, 'I got to ride inside the bus today!'"

Specific images contribute significantly in almost every genre. Sports announcers use specific images to create what writers call "color commentary." For example, John Madden could have made the general statement, "He's a slow runner." Instead, he added color commentary by painting a specific image: "Our scouts had him timed in the 40-yard dash as slightly slower than a cloud on a windless day."

Jim Murray, the Pulitzer Prize-winning sports columnist, made his reputation with his specific images. Instead of simply writing, "Linebacker Bruce Smith goes after the ball aggressively," Murray paints the specific image: "It's as if Smith is a bear and a halfback has one of his cubs."

Comedians and sports writers follow a similar pattern—a pattern once used by talk-show hosts. The host begins with an abstract statement like, "It is so hot today." His companion asks, "How hot is it?" Then the host responds with a specific image like "It's so hot, I poured McDonald's coffee in my lap to cool off." Or "It's so hot, the state bird is now a fried chicken."

Often sports commentators use similes to create their images as in these comments on a halfback:

General Statement

He is hard to tackle.

Specific Examples with Similes

It's like tackling a locomotive.

—Glen Holtzman

It's like standing blindfolded in the middle of Interstate 75, dodging the cars and trying to tackle the biggest truck out there.

—Gary Burley

Another approach is to begin with "Each time. . ." or "Every time. . ." and follow with **hyperbole** (extravagant exaggeration) as in these examples:

General Statement

He is hard to tackle.

Specific Examples with Hyperbole

Each time you tackle him, it reduces your I.Q.

—Pete Wysocki

Every time I tackle him, I hear a dice game going on inside my mouth.

—Don Burroughs

In the activity on the next page, create your own color commentary using either a simile (with *like* or *as*) or hyperbole. Read each generalization and follow it with a specific image.

For some interesting examples of hyperbole, go to http://www.worsleyschool.net/socialarts/hyperbole/hyperbole2.html or http://www.dowlingcentral.com/MrsD/area/literature/Terms/hyperbole.html

For similes, check out Think Tank Idea Bank at http://www.datafilebank.com/similesgalore/csmenumain.htm or Eve Merriam's simile poem at http://volweb.utk.edu/Schools/bedford/harrisms/1poe.htm

TIP Don't be concerned with making your color commentary humorous. Any interesting image will work. Also, feel free to switch the gender in any of the statements.

Name _____ Period _____

Create Color Commentary

1 General Statement She is so fast.

Specific Example

1 _____

2 General Statement He is incredibly strong.

Specific Example

2 _____

3 General Statement Each time she spikes the ball. . . .

Specific Example

3 _____

4 General Statement Every time he carries the ball. . . .

Specific Example

4 _____

Strategies for the Grammar of Conventions

How important is grammar? Dave Barry, author and humorist, makes this observation:

I cannot overemphasize the importance of good grammar. Suppose you are being interviewed for a job as an airplane pilot, and your prospective employer asks you if you have any experience, and you answer, "Well, I ain't never actually flied no actual airplanes or nothing, but I got several pilot-style hats and several friends who I like to talk about airplanes with." If you answer this way, the prospective employer will immediately realize that you have ended your sentence with a preposition.

—Dave Barry, "What Is and Ain't Grammatical"

Although Dave Barry is joking, it is true that your grammatical knowledge can make a difference in your life. If you are going to be a world-class athlete or a rock star or a movie idol, then grammatical errors may not seem like an important factor in your income. However, chances are that someday you are going to be seeking a better-paying position with some company or organization. When that time arrives, your grammatical habits may make the difference in whether or not you get the job.

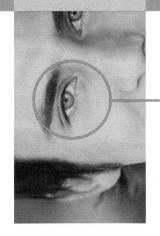

Name _____ Period _____

ACTIVITY 1   Discover the Templates in Your Mind

Try this experiment and see how your mind is programmed for grammatical patterns. Read the following sentences, which are made up of nonsense words mixed with a few prepositions and articles. With each sentence, substitute real words in the blanks. **Keep the words and endings indicated in blue, substituting only for the nonsense words.**

1. **The nold zan, moding into the aklit sorner, vogged the tolmer.**

1 _____ _____ _____ _____
  _____ _____ _____ _____.

2. **The mooklar delted the gonkers from the volute pag.**

2 _____ _____ _____ _____
  _____ _____ _____.

3. **Luk and futly, the wajug toraged toward the plonker.**

3 _____ _____ _____ _____
  _____ _____ _____.

4. **Vaming the garb nuck, the loggen jowed the quan into the dowit.**

4 _____ _____ _____ _____
  _____ _____ _____
  _____ _____ _____.

Were you able to create four sentences that make sense? This was probably not difficult. Why? Since the time you were born, you have been learning grammatical patterns—patterns that enable you to communicate in English. Without knowledge of these patterns, you would be unable to make a simple statement like, "Are you going to the game tonight?" Instead, you would jumble words in a random order, creating statements like, "Going are game to tonight you the?"

If you are still uncertain about your knowledge of grammatical structures, try this. Examine the words you substituted for these nonsense words in the first two sentences: *zan, sorner, tolmer, mooklar, gonkers,* and *pag.* Can you tell which part of speech all of these represent? What about the words *vogged* and *delted?*

As a speaker of English, your brain has learned patterns for arranging words to make sense. However, to solve many grammatical problems, you need to be able to consciously recognize these basic grammatical structures. This section on conventions will help you do this and much more.

To help reinforce your recognition of nouns, verbs, adjectives, adverbs, and participles, you are going to try imitating a nonsense passage about Roscoe, the orangutan, pictured at the right.

Think about how you might paint Roscoe with words. Consider which details to emphasize; what general impression

do you want to convey? Imagine that Roscoe is amused by something he sees. He might be looking at another orangutan, a trainer, an onlooker, a bird, or some unusual object. Visualize the scene.

Name _____ Period _____

ACTIVITY 2 Painting the Template Images

Read this nonsense paragraph about Roscoe.

Tigoling at the peler zugroo, Roscoe sagored and kaked. When the zugroo clooted sumly and turked a mook pun at the wertip, Roscoe berked and veeped, cronking over a putim and baloking at the nook.

In the space provided, rewrite the paragraph, replacing the nonsense words with recognizable ones.

To help you get started, review the list of action verbs at the right and select a few to include in your paragraph. Notice that if you change the *–ed* ending to an *–ing* form, these verbs become participles and can be used in place of the nonsense words *tigoling, cronking,* and *baloking.*

smiled	grinned	beamed	smirked
sneered	mocked	laughed	snickered
gazed	stared	glanced	watched
gawked	analyzed	examined	studied
scrutinized	considered	jogged	trotted
dashed	hustled	scampered	scurried
scrambled	crawled	sauntered	leaped
hopped	vaulted	bounced	bounded
flinched	winced	recoiled	ambushed
pounced	screamed	bellowed	howled
shrieked	bawled	whooped	hooted
screeched	yelped	squealed	

_____

_____

_____

_____

_____

ACTIVITY 2 continued

Now, categorize the words you created and list them on the chart below. If a space is shaded, it means that no word is available for that blank.

Nouns	Verbs	Adjectives	Adverbs	Participles

The remaining words—those not on the chart—will include these prepositions, articles, and conjunctions: *at, the, and, when, the, and, a, at, the, and, over, a.*

Name _____ Period _____

ACTIVITY 3 You're Fired! / You're Hired!

Imagine that you are part of a personnel team (your teacher will divide the class into groups for this) in charge of hiring employees for a new division of Culture Unlimited, a combination music and book store opening near your hometown. The store will be one of the largest and most exclusive in the country—designed to attract middle and upper class clientele with hard-to-find CDs and rare books as well as popular titles.

Your personnel team needs to fill a wide variety of positions, ranging from clerks and secretaries to sales personnel and middle managers. The company president has directed you to hire people who are intelligent and well-educated—individuals you can rely on to help this new business establish an image of quality.

Hundreds of cover letters and résumés have been sent to your company. As a way of selecting which résumés to examine, your team has decided to sort job candidates based on their cover letters. Read these letters (pages 77–79) and rank them from best (1) to worst (6), recording your rankings in the shaded boxes next to each name. Be prepared to discuss each letter with your team to help create a group ranking.

Emma Dyer _____
Reasons for the ranking _____
_____

Lulu Kabong _____
Reasons for the ranking _____
_____

John Nobel _____
Reasons for the ranking _____
_____

Homer Shnoz _____
Reasons for the ranking _____
_____

Betty Guesston _____
Reasons for the ranking _____
_____

Louis Lamore _____
Reasons for the ranking _____
_____

76

continued

ACTIVITY 3 continued

Mr. Jay Worthington
Culture Unlimited
16800 Corporate Lane
Shalersville, Ohio 44266

6915 Flatbush Drive
Irvine, CA 26788
216-737-4545
edyer@somenet.com

Dear Sir:

I understand that Culture Unlimited is expanding it's stores in Ohio and would like to apply for a management position with your company. Having been unemployed for 13 months, I am anxious to locate a stable position with a good salary and reasonable benefits.

I was last employed with the accounting department of Enron for a few years. Prior to that, I held a position in the research department of Udder Industries just before they went bankrupt. For a year I been working with Swifty Airlines in the assembly division but was released when a cargo door blew off the airplane at 20,000 feet. As I'm sure the company officials will tell you, the problem weren't my fault. It was mostly an error with their quality control people.

Enclosed you will find more detailed information on my resume.

Thank you,
Emma Dyer

PS: I am anxiously awaiting your reply.

1883 Orange Peel Drive
Sarasota, Florida 33789
(331) 673-2109

Dear Mr. Worthington:

I want to be a secretery and work with your companey in Ohio. I think your company is a highly respected organisation and I would be proud to work for it. I have taken courses at Cold Creek University and earned mostly good grades. I also have a good knowledge of your company and would make a great secretery.

I can type fast and worked for a short time as a secretery for Arc Industries. Naturally, I don't expect to start at the top, but I feel my enthusiasm will someday lead me their. I know you're anxious to look at my exact qualifications, so I have atached a resume.

If you would like to meet for an interview, that would be real nice.

Sincerely,
Lulu Kabong

Mr. Jay Worthington
Culture Unlimited
16800 Corporate Lane
Shalersville, Ohio 44266

2618 Woodley Place
Alvin, Texas 12008
316-693-7723

Dear Mr. Worthington:

Please consider me for a position in your company's planned expansion program in Ohio. Your emphasis on developing a "leisure lounge" atmosphere to market reading material and music interests me greatly.

For the past three years I've been working with Borders stores in Texas, directing market research and developing sales training programs for field representatives. Each of my field representatives were among the top sales personnel in the company.

Recently, I've been attending Tritech College to further my education with an advanced degree in sales and marketing. The courses I've taken and the experience I've had should be an asset in developing the new directions your company is taking.

The attached resume details my qualifications and work history. I would appreciate your kind consideration in examining my application, and I look forward to hearing from you.

Regards,
John Nobel

WANTED

An alert, aggressive employer who will recognize an alert, aggressive sales production manager!!!!!

Dear Mr. Worthington:

Shnoz is my name and books is my game. CDs too. I can make you're business boom. If you really want to increase production, if you want people who can speak good. Then, I'm the person who can get the job done. I know that the important job of managers are to present a positive image. I'm a mean, lean, managing machine!

Want to know more? Check my enclosed resume. It's loaded with good stuff.

Absolutely the Best,
Homer Shnoz

ACTIVITY 3 continued

5820 Faulkner Ave.
Slippery Rock, Penna. 44277
(212) 762-3948

Mr. Jay Worthington
Culture Unlimited
16800 Corporate Lane
Shalersville, Ohio 44266

Dear Mr. Worthington:

In the latest issue of the Wall Street Journal, I read of your plans to expand Culture Unlimited by opening a new CD and book division in Ohio, using an innovative "Leisure Lounge" concept. Considering that I know sales promotion, and particularly know book and CD promotion! I believe I could lead your company in making a successful entry into the Ohio market.

My expertise spans 15 years and includes extensive experience in designing advertising programs and establishing retail networks. I helped spearhead the highly profitable "Creature Feature" campaign for Simon DVDs.

Next week I will be in the Cleveland area on business and would like an opportunity to stop by and discuss my employment possibilities with you. Enclosed is my resume with additional information. I look forward to hearing from you at your earliest convenience.

Sincerely,
Betty Guesston

---

543 Pordunk Lane
Yokum, Arizona 66729

Culture Unlimited
16800 Corporate Lane
Shalersville, Ohio 44266

Dear Mr. Worthington:

A friend of mine, George Hunzel, suggested I apply for one of your recent job openings. I been worked in various businesses—ranging from grocery clerk to gas station attendent. Also, I have read several books like "War of the Worlds," which has great special effects.

I'm looking for a position with a good company, as my current employer is a jerk and complains about every little thing like when a person don't get to work exactly on time. I believe if a manager wants to be effective, they have to act nice to workers. So I'm looking to move to a better situation where the company manager isn't so unreasonable. Your company Culchure Unlimited sounds like the place for me considering your leasure thing and all. Please take a look at my resume and consider me for a position in your industry.

Respectfully,
Louis Lamore

Name _____ Period _____

After your group has ranked each cover letter from best to worst, write an essay comparing and contrasting the letter you ranked as best with the one you ranked as worst. Compare and contrast at least four items that influenced your choices.

_____

_____

_____

_____

_____

_____

_____

_____

_____

_____

_____

_____

_____

_____

ACTIVITY 4

The Shalersville University Occupational Inventory of Grammatical Knowledge

As demonstrated in the research of Shalersville University's Edward McCormick, Ph.D. (formerly with the University of Mottsburg), an individual's grammatical habits correlate with his or her income. The fewer grammatical mistakes an individual makes, the more money that individual tends to earn. The test that follows will show you with 85 to 95 percent accuracy your future income level based on your current grammatical knowledge.

Instructions Mark each sentence as "C" if it is grammatically correct, "I" if it is incorrect, or "?" if you are uncertain. Wrong answers count for a minus two. A question mark, indicating you are uncertain, only counts for a minus one. Keep in mind that errors may be of any variety: punctuation, capitalization, spelling, or usage.

_____ 1. When the fire started, we was downtown at the movies.

_____ 2. The principal didn't have no business accusing Josh.

_____ 3. Luther and I were there and saw the whole show.

_____ 4. Each 30-second television ad shown during the Super Bowl costs sponsors on the average of $1.9 million dollars. Partly because of the 85 to 90 million viewers who tune in.

_____ 5. In some playing cards, Charlemagne is represented by the king of hearts, Caesar is represented by the king of diamonds, Alexander the Great is represented by the king of clubs, and King David is represented by the king of spades.

_____ 6. During the civil war, a bullet went through Clara Barton's sleeve and killed the wounded soldier she was treating.

_____ 7. After the long day of practice, we sat down to rest.

_____ 8. With Texas Hold 'Em card players, they're ability to bluff plays a key role.

_____ 9. Winning fifty chess games and drawing six Grandmaster George Koltanowski played 56 opponents blindfolded.

_____ 10. Maria Sharapova is a Wimbledon Champion, a multimillionaire, and also does very well acting.

_____ 11. The large group of students are going in a bus instead of a van.

_____ 12. There is hardly no problem more difficult than national defense.

_____ 13. Dan's ability to sing certainly surprised Albert and I.

continued

Name _____ Period _____

_____ 14. Edgar Allan Poe did not have a steady handle as you can see from his handwriting.

_____ 15. Don Braddick landed a 3450 pound great white shark in the Atlantic Ocean off the coast of New York but Frank Mundus, the captain of the charter boat, is given some credit.

_____ 16. Mark Twain once wrote a novel about his steam boat experience on the mississippi river.

_____ 17. Before buying the car, we set down with the owner and discussed repairs.

_____ 18. Their here to see the new movie.

_____ 19. Before the Aswan Dam was constructed, the Egyptians used the flooding of the Nile as a natural enrichment for their crops.

_____ 20. Stephen King has dreamed of attacking insects, falling elevators and also zombies who walk in the night.

_____ 21. The books pages were yellowed with age.

_____ 22. Having watched 12 hours of Twilight Zone reruns, the special finally came to and end.

_____ 23. The halfback turned, spun, and plowed through the line.

_____ 24. Neither the participants nor the tournament director did their job.

_____ 25. The Peregrine falcon which can reach speeds of over 175 miles per hour has been sighted passing small airplanes.

_____ 26. Will someone let the dog's in if it rains?.

_____ 27. The game of Sizzle ended, having used all of the game cards.

_____ 28. The collection included books by Jay Leno Dave Barry and Steve Martin.

_____ 29. Each of the plans has their problems.

_____ 30. Plant smuggling which generates five billion dollars a year is a growing illegal business.

View the PowerPoint list of answers to score your paper. Mark those items that you missed on the Confidential Score Sheet on the following page. This is confidential and will be used to help your teacher determine which items you need to spend time reviewing.

ACTIVITY 5   Confidential Score Sheet

Each grammatical error listed at the right reflects two questions on the test. If you missed one or both of the two numbers listed, circle the name of the indicated grammatical concept. For example, if you missed question 11, you would circle "Subject-Verb Agreement." If you missed both numbers 4 and 14, you would circle "Sentence Fragments." Identifying the items you missed will help your teacher decide which concepts need instruction. Don't be concerned if you missed a lot of these. After all, they are the most commonly made errors.

As Dr. McCormick points out, grammatical patterns correlate with income. Count the number of items you missed on the test and calculate your projected salary and occupational level.

Fifteen of the Most Common Grammatical Errors Identified by Question Number

1 and 11	Subject-Verb Agreement
2 and 12	Double Negatives
3 and 13	Pronoun as Subject and Object
4 and 14	Sentence Fragments
5 and 15	Run-on Sentences/Comma Splices/Fused Sentences
6 and 16	Capitalization of Proper Nouns
7 and 17	Confusion with *sit, sat, set*
8 and 18	Confusion with *their* and *they're/your* and *you're/it's* and *its*
9 and 19	Comma after an Introductory Element
10 and 20	Lack of Parallel Structure
21 and 26	Possessive Apostrophe Error
22 and 27	Dangling Participle
23 and 28	Commas in a Series
24 and 29	Pronoun and Antecedent
25 and 30	Restrictive and Nonrestrictive Clauses

Inventory Rankings

Points Missed	Projected Salary	Occupational Level
0 to -1	$200,000 and above	top executive
-2 to -3	$90,000 to $200,000	upper management
-4 to -5	$60,000 to $90,000	key personnel
-6 to -8	$25,000 to $60,000	semi-skilled
-9 to -10	$10,000 to $25,000	unskilled
-11 or more	$0 to $10,000	unemployable

Introduction to the Express Line Checkouts and Proofreading Warm-ups

According to scholars who have researched our language habits, if you use certain grammatical expressions, educated people will perceive you as unintelligent and uneducated. These assumptions may be wrong. Many people who use what is termed "poor grammar" have simply learned these patterns in the environment where they were raised. Grammatical knowledge has very little to do with intelligence or competence.

However, in spite of the evidence to the contrary, employers, personnel directors, and well-educated adults tend to assume that poor grammatical usage does indicate low intelligence and a lack of competence.

Looking at a 300- to 400-page grammar handbook might make you think that learning grammatical conventions is impossible. But you can shortcut this process by focusing on (1) the errors that occur most frequently and (2) the errors that are status-producing, meaning they are errors educated individuals easily recognize. Researchers have shown that a surprising 91.5 percent of all errors in student writing come from only 20 items.

In this section of the activities book, you are going to examine several of these critical errors using an "Express Line Checkout," an idea suggested by teacher/author Jeff Anderson.

Here is how the express line checkout works. Just as you can quickly check out four or five items in a grocery store express line, you can quickly check for three or four grammatical problems when proofreading a paper. The idea is to examine each paper for only a few selected errors. In addition, you will be examining Proofreading Warm-ups activities for only two or three errors. This will help prepare you for the more complex checkouts.

Working through the Proofreading Warm-up and the Express Line Checkouts will help you gain control over status-producing errors. This is your chance to increase your social status by several levels and boost your future income by thousands of dollars.

Grammatical Item for Express Line Checkout 1

Study the explanations of each cluster of grammatical concepts that follow and then exit through the Express Line Checkout by proofreading for the items you have just studied.

This first cluster of grammatical errors just deals with one problem: subject-verb agreement, but it includes several tricky examples.

Subject-Verb Agreement Questions 1 and 11

Writers often create ungrammatical language to portray rough, uneducated characters. Robert Louis Stevenson, for example, characterizes Long John Silver by having him say, "You comes and tells me of it plain." Yet, in spite of his incorrect grammar, we soon learn that Long John is extremely intelligent and shrewd.

Unless, like Stevenson, you are using incorrect grammar to build a character, follow this rule. With single subjects (*he, library, cat, Chicago,* or *mountain*), use a singular verb like *was* and *is*. "**He was** there." "The **cat is** sleeping."

If the subject refers to more than one item (*we, restaurants, cats, towns, hats*) use a plural verb. "**We were** there." "The **cats are** sleeping." Here are a few more examples:

Incorrect   His **eyes was** reduced to chinks, and diverging wrinkles appeared round them, extending upon his countenance like the rays in a rudimentary sketch of the rising sun.

Correct   His **eyes were** reduced to chinks, and diverging wrinkles appeared round them, extending upon his countenance like the rays in a rudimentary sketch of the rising sun.

—Thomas Hardy

Singular subjects like *cat, she, house, horse,* and *bottle* go with a singular verbs such as *is* or *was,* as in "The **bottle was** empty." Compare the two sentences below.

Incorrect   **He were** hunted in very much the same fashion as his prototype, the grizzly.

Correct   **He was** hunted in very much the same fashion as his prototype, the grizzly.

—Bret Harte

Tricky Example The Prepositional Phrase Problem

Tricky examples are missed by even the best students. If you missed number 11 on the Shalersville Inventory, you fell victim to an unusual example of subject-verb agreement: an inserted prepositional phrase.

Incorrect   **Each** of the sled dogs **were** well-trained.

What you hear can deceive you. "Dogs were" sounds right, but "dogs" is not the subject of the sentence. The subject is *Each*. The inserted prepositional phrase *of the sled dogs* has no effect on the subject-verb agreement.

Correct   **Each** of the sled dogs **was** well-trained.

Tricky Example The Expletive Problem

The expletive *there* is a false subject and can lead to one of the most common errors among well-educated individuals. It is not unusual to hear television commentators use incorrect expressions like, "There's a lot of reasons," or "There's a number of things." The rule is to ignore *there* when deciding on subject-verb agreement. Be particularly cautious when the words *there* and *is* are joined with a contraction. Fewer individuals make this same error when using *There is.* Here are a few incorrect and corrected examples:

Incorrect   **There's** no roads of any kind in the valley—nothing but a labyrinth of footpaths twisting and turning among the thickets without end.

Correct   **There are** no roads of any kind in the valley—nothing but a labyrinth of footpaths twisting and turning among the thickets without end.   —Herman Melville

Incorrect   **There's** some things too horrible, too hideous, too repulsive for description—Bukawai's face was one of these.

Correct   **There are** some things too horrible, too hideous, too repulsive for description—Bukawai's face was one of these.

—Edgar Rice Burroughs

Tricky Example Group Nouns

Nouns that identify a collection such as *group, team,* or *gang* act just like a single noun. However, when a prepositional phase is added before the verb, a writer can be fooled.

Incorrect   The **group** of performers **were** late to the gig.

Correct   The **group** of performers **was** late to the gig.

So far, we've only looked at one type of error. However, because subject-verb agreement is a difficult problem, we're going to take just this one type of error through the first express line.

ACTIVITY 6 Express Line Checkout 1

Examine the passage below and try to find the four incorrect subject-verb agreements. Circle each error you locate.

Uncle Harold was famous for lying. Each of his stories were questionable. There's some stories that I thought were lies for sure, but I enjoyed listening to him.

He had once been shot right between the eyes. He told me so himself. It was during World War I. As an under-aged boy, he had run away from home, enlisted in the Marine Corps, and been shipped to France. There, a group of the Kaiser's soldiers were tracking him, and eventually one soldier shot him right between the eyes.

It was a miracle it hadn't killed him, and I said so the evening he told me about it. He explained that Marines on his team was so tough they didn't need miracles. I was now approaching the age of skepticism, and though it was risky business challenging adults, I was tempted to say, "Swear on the Bible?" I did not dare go this far, but I did get a hint of doubt into my voice by repeating his words as a question.

"Right between the eyes?"

"Right between the eyes," he said. "See this scar?"

He placed a finger on his forehead just above the bridge of his nose. "That's all the mark it left," he said.

"I don't see any scar," I said.

—Adapted from *Growing Up* by Russell Baker

Note This passage was modified to include errors that were not in the original. The original can be viewed in the PowerPoint.

Grammatical Items for Express Line Checkout 2

Double Negatives Questions 2 and 12

A double negative occurs when a writer or speaker places two negative words in the same sentence. For example, during a radio interview on the Bob and Tom Show, music star John Mellencamp commented,

"The soundman knows he **don't do nothing.**"

—The Bob and Tom Show, 3/24/06

Some grammarians argue that a double negative creates a confusing reversal in the minds of readers. A minus plus a minus, they say, equals a plus. If Mellencamp says, "The soundman knows he don't do nothing," that technically means the soundman *does* do something. Educated individuals recognize the double negative as an error. For a popular singer, this poses no problem, but for an average person seeking a job that requires someone who is articulate, avoiding double negatives is important.

To avoid this problem, examine your writing for combinations of these negatives:

no, not, none, no one, nothing, nowhere, neither, nobody, never, doesn't, isn't, wasn't, wouldn't, couldn't, shouldn't, won't, can't, don't.

Be especially aware of combinations like "don't do nothing," "wasn't nobody," and "couldn't never."

Here is an example to review:

Incorrect I **never** saw **nothing** like it before—unless it was a skull.

Correct I **never** saw **anything** like it before—unless it was a skull.

—Edgar Allan Poe

Tricky Example The *hardly* Problem

A few adverbs are classified as negatives and should not be used with another negative. The most common of these adverbs are the words *hardly, scarcely,* and *rarely.* For example, notice the difference in these sentences:

Incorrect The window was so wet I **couldn't hardly** see.

Correct The window was so wet I **couldn't** see.

—James Joyce

Pronoun as Subject and Object
Questions 3 and 13

Personal pronouns can lead to two types of common errors:
(1) pronouns that incorrectly function as subjects and (2) pronouns that incorrectly function as objects.

Pronouns That Function as Subjects Subjective personal pronouns are those designated for use as the subject of a sentence and include *I, you, she, he, it, we, you,* and *they.* These pronouns are the subjects of the sentence and tell the thing or person who is doing something. These words are used in this type of slot:

_____ was (or were) there.

In sentences where pronouns follow a linking verb such as *is, are, was, were, am,* and other forms of *be* and rename the subject, a subject pronoun should also be used.

Incorrect   It is **him.**
This is **her.**
It is **us** who should lead the charge.

Correct   It is **he.**
This is **she.**
It is **we** who should lead the charge.

Pronouns That Function as Objects Objective personal pronouns fit in this type of slot:

The pit bull lunged toward _____.

Six pronouns fit this slot: *me, her, him, it, us,* and *them.* These are direct or indirect objects of the verb, or objects of a preposition. You will find that objective pronouns usually follow a preposition.

Tricky Example   The Name-Pronoun Problem

A common error occurs when a name is used with a pronoun.

Incorrect   **Owen and me were** throwing rocks into the Squamscott, the saltwater river.

Correct   **Owen and I were** throwing rocks into the Squamscott, the saltwater river.

—John Irving

Incorrect   Leon gave the tickets **to Roberto and I.**

Correct   Leon gave the tickets **to Roberto and me.**

Name _____ Period _____

Proofreading Warm-up

The passage below is a warm-up for the Express Line Checkout 2 that follows. In this passage you will find three errors. Look for double negatives and incorrect pronouns. Circle each error you are able to find.

As we drove nearer, it proved to be, to our excitement, a small herd of six buffalo, hunchbacked, shaggy, wading shoulder high through the snow, packed tightly together, trailing shawls of white steamy breath behind them. We watched them for perhaps ten minutes until they were out of sight. Finally, there wasn't hardly a sound. We were just going to start up the car when suddenly, from the interior of the dark mesh of trees, our strolled an enormous old bull buffalo.

"It's him," Lee said, "the leader."

On to the snowfield, white as a banqueting-cloth, he sauntered out, his beard swinging to his rolling walk, his horns sharp-curved as bows, his great forehead and massive shoulders a mass of dark ringlets, the breath from his nostrils making two cumulus clouds of steam ahead of him as he moved. Slowly, like a portly, well-made man of substance taking his constitutional, he moved across the white expanse. Here the snow was not so deep, so it only came up to his knees. He moved ponderously across until he was perhaps two hundred yards from the tree line. Then he paused and mused, his breath forming a cloud around his face, entangling itself in the fur of his forehead and shoulders. We had never seen nothing so majestic. Then he sauntered after the herd, of which we had no doubt he was king. Slowly, mediatively, like a huge, dark cloud, he moved across the snow and disappeared.

—Adapted from *How to Shoot an Amateur Naturalist* by Gerald Durrell

Note This passage was modified to include errors that were not in the original.

Sentence Fragments Questions 4 and 14

Sentence fragments are sometimes like icebergs that break off from the mainland. If you look at the sentence that comes before the fragment, you can frequently see how they might once have once been attached. Look at the following example:

Incorrect Hatsuyo Nakamura, weak and destitute, began a courageous struggle to keep her children and herself alive. **Which would last for many years.**

Correct Hatsuyo Nakamura, weak and destitute, began a courageous struggle to keep her children and herself alive, **which would last for many years.**

—John Hersey

The problem with many fragments is that when they are spoken, they sound correct. The pause before or after the fragment doesn't distinguish between a period and a comma. This is why over 75 percent of mistakes in written English cannot be committed in speech. To locate fragments, look for incomplete structures like these:

Structure	Fragment
Participial Phrase	Turning down the slope.
Subordinate Clause	Since she suggested the change.
Prepositional Phrase	With a crowd of three thousand.
Relative Pronoun Clause	Which won the game.

If you suspect a fragment, read the words aloud and ask yourself if they sound like a complete sentence. Usually, you can recognize the incomplete structure. For example, if you say out loud, "turning down the slope," your mind demands completion. You ask, "Turning down the slope, what?" or "What happened turning down the slope?"

Tricky Example Purposeful Fragments

Authors play with words and sometimes use purposeful fragments. Here is one example:

It was 2 p.m. Thirty below. No wind. Totally dark. My boots squeaked on the dry, granular snow as I walked. My breath froze in the air and coated the fur of my parka hood white.

—Joe McGinnis

McGinnis is a skilled writer who can enhance the significance of a scene with fragments. He knows he has created fragments and recognizes how they can sometimes create an artistic effect. If you create a fragment and your artistic intent creates more confusion than artistry, your teacher will no doubt mark it as an error. So it is best to avoid all fragments.

In all of the Express Line Checkouts, including the one that follows, assume that the passage is written as a formal paper and mark any fragments as incorrect.

Name _____

Period _____

ACTIVITY 8 Express Line Checkout 2

Examine the passage below and try to find the six errors of the following types: (1) double negatives, (2) subject and object pronouns, and (3) fragments. Circle each error you find.

Sibling rivalry in our family began the first day I brought our second son home from the hospital. His brother looked at him and said, "Maybe later we could get a dog."

The rivalry was subtle at first. He'd stand on the baby's windpipe. Or trap him under the casters of his playpen. At the grocery, he pushed his cart into a blank wall and left him.

"What's with you and your brother?" I'd ask.

"It's him. He's dumb. He doesn't do nothing. He just slobbers and eats the labels off of cans."

It hardly never got any better between his brother and he. When he stopped slobbering! He began to spit!

—Adapted from *Family—the Ties that Bind and Gag* by Erma Bombeck

Note This passage was modified to include errors that were not in the original.

Grammatical Items for Express Line Checkout 3

Run-on Sentences / Comma Splices / Fused Sentences Sentences Questions 5 and 15

Run-ons, comma splices, and fused sentences are three terms used to describe the same punctuation problem: joining two sentences incorrectly. Although many English teachers refer to these three problems as run-on sentences, grammarians make this distinction:

Run-on A run-on joins two or more sentences with only a coordinating conjunction (*and, but, or, nor, for, so, yet*). The writer leaves out the comma needed with the conjunction to join two sentences. See the incorrect example and the correction that follows.

Incorrect He was emaciated **and** he was smoking sixty cigarettes a day.

Correct He was emaciated, **and** he was smoking sixty cigarettes a day.

—Truman Capote

Comma Splice A comma splice joins two sentences with only a comma, as in this incorrect example:

Incorrect A big foaming sea came out of the mist, it made for the ship, roaring wildly, and in its rush it looked as mischievous and discomposing as a madman with an axe.

Correct A big foaming sea came out of the mist. It made for the ship, roaring wildly, and in its rush it looked as mischievous and discomposing as a madman with an axe.

—Joseph Conrad

Fused Sentence A fused sentence joins two independent clauses together without a comma or a coordinating conjunction.

Incorrect That he had this power frightened **him he** decided not to tell.

Correct That he had this power frightened him. **He** decided not to tell.

—Lois Lowry

Tricky Example *However*

The word *however* does not join sentences. It must have a semicolon with it when located between them. *However* is an interrupter like *furthermore*. Here are two examples to review:

Incorrect In Cleveland there is legislation moving forward to ban people from wearing pants that fit too low, **however,** there is a lot of opposition from the plumbers' union.

Correct In Cleveland there is legislation moving forward to ban people from wearing pants that fit too low; **however,** there is a lot of opposition from the plumbers' union.

—Conan O'Brien

The average sentence length of a popular magazine article runs between 15 and 20 words. University freshmen average 20 words per sentence when they write. To locate run-on sentences and comma splices, search for long sentences—those that run over 20 words. Don't count each sentence word by word. Simply survey your writing for sentences that seem long. Then read each suspected sentence aloud and listen for natural pauses.

Sentences can only be joined in two ways: (1) a comma and a coordinate conjunction—*and, or, for, nor, but, so*—and (2) a semicolon.

TIP The word *however* can be dropped into the middle of one sentence. In this case, it is set off with commas as in these examples:

In these checks and impossibilities, however, we find our advantage.

—Ralph Waldo Emerson

Such principles, however, are not trivial to the philosopher.

—Bertrand Russell

ACTIVITY 9 Proofreading Warm-Up

Examine the passage below and try to find the three errors. Look for problems with (1) a run-on, (2) a comma splice, (3) a fused sentence, and (4) *however*. Circle each error you find.

BLAM!

The kitchen door flew open, it had been left ajar just a crack to let the air come in to cool the ham. I rushed to the kitchen, however, just in time to see the blue-ticked Bumpus hounds roar through the screen door in a great, roiling mob the leader of the pack—the one that almost got the old man every day—leaped high onto the table and grabbed the butt end of the ham in his enormous slavering jaws. The rest of the hounds—squealing, yapping, panting, rolling over one another in a frenzy of madness—pounded out the kitchen door after Big Red, trailing brown sugar and pineapple slices behind him. They were in and out in less than five seconds. The screen door hung on one hinge, its screen ripped and torn and dripping with gravy and they went out just like that.

—Adapted from *A Christmas Story* by Jean Shepherd

Capitalization of Proper Nouns Questions 6 and 16

The capitalization of proper nouns can be understood by viewing nouns through a zoom lens. For example, imagine that you are sitting in the last row at a country music concert featuring a number of country music stars. A performer walks out on the stage. From where you are seated, which seems like a mile away, you can only tell that it is a performer. The word *performer* is a common noun that could be used to label a number of specific singers. However, when you look through your binoculars and zoom in for a close-up, you can see the performer is country singer Trisha Yearwood. The name *Trisha Yearwood* is a proper noun. It identifies a specific, one-of-a-kind item.

Proper nouns consist of all sorts of specific items—specific people, places, titles, religions, races, government departments, cities, and so on. A few examples include *Chicago, Mount Helena, the Federal Bureau of Investigation, President Lincoln, the Beatles,* and *the Taj Mahal.*

Tricky Example Proper Adjectives

A concept related to proper nouns creates an occasional problem—the proper adjective. Proper adjectives are simply adjectives created from proper nouns such as *American* created from the proper noun *America, German* from *Germany,* and *Mexican* from *Mexico.*

Most proper adjectives end with an *-an* or *-ian,* with a few exceptions such as *French* derived from *France* and *Chinese* from *China.* Proper adjectives are capitalized.

ACTIVITY 10

Creating Proper Nouns

Look at each common noun on the left and write one specific proper noun in the column on the right.

Common Noun	Proper Noun	Common Noun	Proper Noun
musical group	_____	name of school	_____
television program	_____	street name	_____
famous artist	_____	holiday	_____
language	_____	birth date	_____
city	_____	river or lake	_____
historical event	_____	store	_____
sports figure	_____	brand of electronics	_____
movie title	_____	country	_____
favorite team	_____	song	_____
friend's name	_____		
book title	_____		

Confusion with *sit, sat, set* Questions 7 and 17

Sit means to recline or rest as in "Sit down and relax." *Sat* is a past tense, meaning it is only used when describing something that happened in the past, as in "She sat here yesterday."

These two words are often confused with the word *set*, which is used when placing something. "Set the book down." "He set the package on the table." You can usually determine if the word *set* is correct by replacing it with the word *put*. If *put* works, then *set* is correct. Examine these examples and write the word you think is appropriate.

Shanna _____ her glass on the edge of the table.

Last week, Deron _____ on the soft recliner.

I watched the cat _____ by the fire.

Confusion with *their* and *they're/your* and *you're/it's* and *its* Questions 8 and 18

These three problems can easily be solved. In all three, the apostrophe *s* and apostrophe *re* represent verbs. The word *they're* means *they are*. The word *you're* means *you are*. *It's* translates into *it is*.

To check if you have used the right word, just substitute the full verb for the apostrophe *s* or the apostrophe *re* and see if the sentence works. For example, notice what happens if you replace the word *they're* with *they are* in this sentence:

Incorrect   **They're** house was cold.

Incorrect   **They are** house was cold.

Correct   **Their** house was cold.

ACTIVITY 11

Express Line Checkout 3

Examine the Mark Twain passage below and try to find examples of each of these errors: (1) run-on sentences, comma splices and fused sentences, (2) capitalization of proper nouns, (3) confusion with *sit, sat,* and *set,* and (4) confusion with *their* and *they're /your* and *you're /it's* and *its.* There are eight places in the following passage where these errors occur. Circle each one you find.

Among my experiments was this, in an hour I taught a cat and a dog to be friends. I sat them in a cage. In another hour I taught them to be friends with a rabbit. In the course of two days I was able to add a fox, a goose, a squirrel, some doves, and finally a monkey. They lived together in peace, even affectionately.

Next, in another cage I confined an irish Catholic from Tipperary and as soon as he seemed tame, I added a scotch Presbyterian from Aberdeen. Next, I added a Turk from Constantinople; a Greek Christian from Crete; an Armenian; a Methodist from the wilds of arkansas; a Buddhist from China; a Brahman from Benares, and finally, a Salvation Army Colonel from Wapping. Then I stayed away two whole days, when I came back to note results, the cage of animals was all right, but in the other their was but a chaos of gory odds and ends of turbans and *fezzes* and plaids and bones and flesh—not a specimen left alive. These reasoning animals had disagreed on a theological detail and carried the matter to a higher court.

—From *Letters from the Earth* by Mark Twain

Note This passage was modified to include errors that were not in the original.

Grammatical Items for Express Line Checkout 4

Comma After an Introductory Element

An introductory element can be a single word, a phrase, or a clause.

Single Introductory Word When a sentence is introduced with a single word, the word is usually an adverb and often ends in -ly. Some typical introductory words include *quickly, ironically, suddenly, finally, yesterday, yet, still, however, nonetheless,* and *often.* Adverbs like these, that begin a sentence, should be set off with a comma. To determine if you have a one-word introductory element, eliminate the word and see if the sentence still makes sense.

Long Introductory Prepositional Phrase When a sentence begins with a long prepositional phrase, the phrase is set off with a comma. For example, notice the punctuation in this sentence:

> **By the time he finds the handle of the nine-man life raft,** he doesn't have time to put on his Mustang survival suit.
>
> —Sebastian Junger

Short Introductory Prepositional Phrase With short prepositional phrases—those with fewer than five words—the writer has the option of omitting the comma. In this sentence, Norman Mailer could have opted to omit the comma after the word *minute,* but decided the sentence clarity was better with it.

> **In the next minute,** Ali proceeded to hit Foreman with a combination as rare as plutonium: a straight right hand followed by a long left hook.
>
> —Norman Mailer

Here is an example of omitting the comma when using a short introductory prepositional phrase:

> **At that moment** a great tawny, glistening shape appeared in the doorway, its solitary eye gleaming.
>
> —Russell Gordon Carter

Introductory Participle Brush Stroke When a participle brush stroke begins a sentence, it is always set off with a comma. Here are a few examples:

> **Running along the ramparts,** bent double, the Abbot cried out, "Stretcher bearers! Over here!"
>
> —Brian Jacques

Shaking with the effort, Beth wrenched her eyes from those burning depths up there beyond the ninth floor, only to see again the horror.

—Harlan Ellison

Introductory Clause with a Subordinate Conjunction

Subordinate conjunctions create clauses that connect to main sentences. The subordinate conjunction requires a companion comma to make the connection. Notice in the first sentence below how the subordinate conjunction *while* sets up the clause and the comma after the word *quietly* works with the subordinate conjunction to connect the idea to the main sentence that follows.

While it's great to see your two-year-old child entertaining himself quietly, you have to stay aware of the fact that it's only going to last ten minutes.

—Ray Romano

If God had wanted us to vote, He would have given us candidates.

—Jay Leno

Tricky Example Gerund Phrase

The gerund phrase looks exactly like a participle brush stroke, but is not added to a sentence. Instead, it is part of the sentence and functions as the subject. To avoid confusion, eliminate the *-ing* phrase in your mind and see if the sentence still makes sense. For example, watch what happens if you eliminate the *-ing* phrase in this sentence:

Gerund Intact **A tramping of sea boots** was heard in the entry.

—Herman Melville

Gerund Eliminated Was heard in the entry.

The remaining words create a fragment, so you know the phrase is a gerund and is needed to complete the sentence. By contrast, eliminating a participle brush stroke leaves a clear and complete sentence. Notice what happens when the participial brush stroke is eliminated from the Jacques sentence, used on page 100.

Participle Brush Stroke Intact **Running along the ramparts,** bent double, the Abbot cried out, "Stretcher bearers! Over here!"

—Brian Jacques

Participle Brush Stroke Eliminated Bent double, the Abbot cried out, "Stretcher bearers! Over here!"

The words that are left after you eliminate the *-ing* phrase still make sense, so you know the phase is a participle brush stroke and not a gerund.

Name _____ Period _____

ACTIVITY 12 Proofreading Warm-Up

This warm-up features three types of introductory elements: a single word, a phrase, and a clause.
Locate the four comma errors and circle the place where a comma is needed.

Actually the most entertaining spectacle of my youth was watching both sides of my family try to interact. Each side obviously had totally different attitudes and approaches to life. At the Italian functions on my father's side there would be hundreds of meatballs made for maybe a dozen people. There was more food than anyone could possibly eat—huge pots, huge portions. And my mother's sister, Aunt Nettie, would be incensed by this. "Oooh, look at the food that's goin' to weeeeste," she'd say in her thick burr. "Oooh, the weeeeste!" If there were more than two lights burning in any room she'd scream, "I can't believe it! All these lights on! The weeeeste of electricity!"

Then, we'd go to Aunt Nettie's house, which was run on the safer side of frugality. Looking back on those days I remember how she kept Coca-Cola in the cupboard, because to refrigerate even one bottle would somehow quadruple the cost of the electricity. There was nothing like the sound of a warm Coke being opened—sort of a long wheezing sssssssss—and then seeing it pour out all foam and no liquid. The foam, accompanied by a nice stale scone, made for a Scottish dream snack.

—Adapted from *Leading with My Chin* by Jay Leno

Note This passage was modified to include errors that were not in the original.

Lack of Parallel Structure Questions 10 and 20

Parallel structures create a powerful rhythm in sentences. However, when a rhythm is started and then broken, it is considered an error in parallelism. Compare these sentences:

Broken Rhythm

The slow, quiet winter was spent telling stories, gossiping, and they made implements and weapons.

Melodic Rhythm

The slow, quiet winter was **spent telling stories, gossiping, making implements and weapons.**

—Jean M. Auel

Broken Rhythm

She cocked her head and narrowed her eyes, and she was twisting her lips in a fashion that said, "Irv. Calm down."

Melodic Rhythm

She **cocked her head and narrowed her eyes and twisted her lips** in a fashion that said, "Irv. Calm down."

—Tom Wolf

Parallel structures involve repetitions of nouns, verbs, adjectives, adverbs, prepositional phrases, participial phrases, relative pronouns, and clauses. The better able you are to recognize structures, the easier it will be for you to hear them and write them.

Possessive Apostrophe Error Questions 21 and 26

How important is it to be grammatically correct if you want the public to view you as competent and educated? What does this sign from a Pittsburgh hospital imply about the quality of the organization?

If you recognized that "womens" should be "women's," would you question the competence of the hospital staff? Similarly, would you question the competence of the people working at the New York beauty salon that advertised this service?

Nail's suggests ownership. The word should be *nails.* The skill involved in painting your nails might not be as critical as the skill for heart surgery. But either way, advertisements filled with errors are not the way to build an image of quality and competence.

Here are some quick tips to help you avoid apostrophe problems. First, think of the apostrophe *s* in terms of ownership.

No Ownership Means No Apostrophe

A Singular Noun *Singular* means "one." With no ownership, it needs no apostrophe. For example, in the following sentence, *musician* describes one person. No ownership is suggested, and no apostrophe is needed.

The **musician** performed last night.

A Plural Noun *Plural* means "multiple," and with no ownership, needs no apostrophe. Like the singular noun, no ownership is involved. For example:

The **musicians** performed last night.

Ownership Creates Two Uses of Apostrophes

A Singular Possessive Noun A singular possessive noun means that one noun possesses or owns something, as in this example:

The **dog's jaw**, as shown in the space between these marks, is too broad in my opinion for a terrier and not broad enough for a mastiff.

—A. Conan Doyle

A Plural Possessive Noun A plural possessive noun means a group possesses something, as in the following example:

The humming of the gnats that danced above the eddies of the stream, the beating of the **dragonflies' wings**, the strokes of the water **spiders' legs**, like oars which had lifted their boat—all these made audible music.

—Ambrose Bierce

When you are debating whether or not to use an apostrophe, ask yourself, "Does the noun own anything in this sentence?" If not, then it should not have an apostrophe.

Tricky Example Two Nouns Showing Possession

With two nouns possessing something, place the apostrophe with the second.

Incorrect   Todd's and Anne's apartment was unusual.

Correct   Todd and Anne's apartment was unusual.

ACTIVITY 13 Express Line Checkout 4

Examine the article below and try to find examples of each of these errors: (1) not placing a comma after an introductory element, (2) not maintaining parallel structure, and (3) not correctly using apostrophes. There are ten places in the following article where these errors occur. Circle each one you find.

The Struggle of Women Artists

When art was at its peak in Italy during the fifteenth and sixteenth century only men were recognized as artists. Women were viewed as lacking in intelligence, lacking in character, and they didn't have enough fortitude. Art academies refused to admit them. Their status in Italian society was comparable to that of a slave.

The popular perception at that time was that women were only good for cleaning, child bearing, and to cook. Any woman who attempted to create art was considered scandalous. Womens rights were nonexistent. Consequently, only a few women in that time period were able to develop as artists, and most of these learned from their fathers who were painters. When a woman did emerge as a master artist very few patrons would buy her art. The women artist's had no choice but to concentrate on one type of painting—the portrait, considered at the time as an inferior artistic expression, rarely done by serious artists.

Female artists such as Frida Kahlo, Kathe Kollwitz, and Georgia O'Keeffe are now regarded as some of history's very best. Yet, some injustices continue today. For example, art history books until only recently have excluded most woman artists. Similarly museum collections for centuries only exhibited male artists.

Fortunately, women are mobilizing to rectify these inequities. In 1985 a group of American women artists founded the Guerilla Girls. Members assumed the names of dead women artists and spread their quest for fairness through billboards, books, plays, workshops, and demonstrations. To attract publicity and focus media attention on issues, the Guerilla Girls wore guerrilla masks at demonstrations. Recently the group has grown to over 100 members and has expanded their concerns beyond art to include issues involving sexism, racism, and to help social injustice.

Grammatical Items for Express Line Checkout 5

Dangling Participles Questions 22 and 27

If your participle brush stroke isn't located close to the noun you are painting, the meaning of the sentence can be jumbled, sometimes with comic effect.

> The female suspect was about 20 years old, white, 5' 4" with long black hair **weighing about 150 pounds.**

The word "dangling" means that the participle is not located close to the noun it modifies. To correct a dangling participle, move the participle brush stroke close to the word it modifies as in this example:

> The female suspect, **weighing about 150 pounds,** was about 20 years old, white, 5' 4", with long black hair.

When writing, visualize your zoom lens capturing a close-up of the image you are describing. Then, to avoid a dangling participle, add your brush stroke close to the words that label that image. Notice how this is done correctly in the sentence above with the word *suspect* and the brush stroke "weighing about 150 pounds."

Tricky Example No Noun Found

Sometimes, when trying to shift a participle brush stroke next to a noun in a sentence, you discover that no noun is included, as in this sentence:

| Incorrect | **Relaxing on the beach, flies** began to buzz around their heads. |

Unless you assume the flies are relaxing, the phrase "relaxing on the beach" refers to an image not represented in the sentence. In this case, you need to insert a noun or pronoun that the participle can connect to. For example, the previous sentence might be rewritten as follows:

| Correct | **Relaxing on the beach, the couple** became annoyed when flies began to buzz around their heads. |

Commas in a Series Questions 23 and 28

Use commas to separate words, phrases, or clauses in a series. When it doesn't break the rhythm and when you have three items in a series, place a conjunction between the last two items. Here are examples of each type of series. Compare not only the correct and incorrect use of commas, but also look at the weak rewrites. It destroys the rhythms.

Words

Incorrect Now, an army is a team. It **lives eats sleeps and fights** as a team.

Weak Rewrite Now, an army is a team. It lives. And sometimes it eats as a team. Also, it sleeps and fights as a team.

Correct Now, an army is a team. It **lives, eats, sleeps, and fights** as a team.

—General George Patton (from the film *Patton*)

A "weak rewrite" shows what happens when a writer fails to take advantage of the power of parallel rhythms. Sometimes, when parallel structures are not used, a weak rewrite can be grammatically correct. But if the writer begins a rhythm and then abandons it, it is considered an error because it jolts the musical flow of ideas and images.

With commas used in a series, some grammarians argue that the comma before the conjunction is optional, but by always including it, you can't go wrong. In the Star Trek example below, the scriptwriters omitted the word *and* after the last comma to create more intensity, and it works.

Phrases

Incorrect These are the voyages of the *Starship Enterprise*, its five-year mission **to explore strange new worlds to seek out new life and new civilizations to boldly go where no man has gone before.**

Weak Rewrite These are the voyages of the *Starship Enterprise*. We have a five-year mission. We're going to explore strange new worlds and look for new life and perhaps new civilizations. We will also go boldly where no one else has gone before.

Correct These are the voyages of the *Starship Enterprise*, its five year mission **to explore strange new worlds, to seek out new life and new civilizations, to boldly go where no man has gone before.**

—Opening statement from the *Star Trek* series

Clauses

Incorrect I have a dream that one day **every valley shall be exalted** and **every hill and mountain shall be made low** the **rough places will be made plain** and **the crooked places will be made straight** and **the glory of the Lord shall be revealed.**

Weak Rewrite I have a dream that one day every valley shall be exalted. Also I believe that hills and mountains shall be made low. In my dream, the rough places will be made plain, and the crooked places will be straightened out as well; and the glory of the Lord shall be revealed.

Correct I have a dream that one day **every valley shall be exalted,** and **every hill and mountain shall be made low;** the **rough places will be made plain,** and **the crooked places will be made straight;** and **the glory of the Lord shall be revealed.**

—Martin Luther King, Jr.

ACTIVITY 14   Proofreading Warm-Up

In this warm-up exercise, the approach is reversed. Circle the examples of (1) participle brush strokes used correctly, (2) commas in a series used correctly, and (3) parallel structures that maintain a rhythm. Locate one example of each of the above items.

What is indifference? Etymologically, the word means "no difference." A strange and unnatural state in which the lines blur between light and darkness, dusk and dawn, crime and punishment, cruelty and compassion, good and evil. What are its courses and inescapable consequences? Is it a philosophy? Is there a philosophy of indifference conceivable? Can one possibly view indifference as a virtue?...

Of course, indifference can be tempting—more than that, seductive. It is so much easier to look away from victims. It is so much easier to avoid such rude interruptions to our work, our dreams, our hopes. It is, after all, awkward, troublesome, to be involved in another person's pain and despair. Yet, for the person who is indifferent, his or her neighbors are of no consequence. And, therefore, their lives are meaningless. Their hidden or even visible anguish is of no interest. Indifference reduces the "Other" to an abstraction.

Over there, behind the black gates of Auschwitz, the most tragic of all prisoners were the "Muselmanner," as they were called. Wrapped in their torn blankets, they would sit or lie on the ground, staring vacantly into space, unaware of who or where they were—strangers to their surroundings. They no longer felt pain, hunger, thirst. They feared nothing. They felt nothing. They were dead and did not know it.

—From the speech *"The Perils of Indifference"* by Elie Wiesel

Agreement Between Pronoun and Antecedent Questions 24 and 29

An antecedent is the word or group of words to which a pronoun refers. Every pronoun must agree with its antecedent in number and gender.

Number (Singular and Plural)

Singular antecedents, such as *everybody, one, anyone, each, man,* and *person,* are matched with a singular pronoun. Singular pronouns include words such as *its, his, her, everyone, anyone, nobody, everybody,* and *anybody.* Here are a few examples of both incorrect and correct antecedents linked to pronouns.

Incorrect   **Each** of these plans has **their** advantages.

Correct   **Each** of these plans has **its** advantages.

Incorrect   **Everyone** must have a license for **their** dog.

Correct   **Everyone** must have a license for **his or her** dog.

Tricky Example A Singular and a Plural Antecedent

When a singular and a plural noun are antecedents joined by *or* or *nor,* the pronoun agrees with the closest antecedent. Observe these examples:

Incorrect   Neither the fox nor the **hounds** knew **his** way through the woods.

Correct   Neither the fox nor the **hounds** knew **their** way through the woods.

Also   Neither the hounds nor the **fox** knew **his**

Correct   way through the woods.

Restrictive and Nonrestrictive Clauses
Questions 25 and 30

A **restrictive clause** is one that is essential to the meaning of a sentence. For example, in the sentence, "The dog that has rabies is near Dion's Burger Hut," the information provided by "that has rabies" is essential to the meaning of the sentence. This important clause is labeled as *restrictive* and is not set off with commas.

By contrast, a **nonrestrictive clause** adds secondary information—information that isn't absolutely necessary to the meaning of the sentence. For example, in the sentence, "The dog, which I believe is a black Labrador, is near Dion's Burger Hut," the information expressed in "which I believe is a black Labrador," isn't essential information. If the sentence is read without this clause, the most important information remains. So the clause is considered nonrestrictive.

Adjective Clauses

Most adjective clauses begin with *who, whom, whose, which,* or *that* and describe a noun. Here are two correct examples—one of a restrictive adjective clause and one of a nonrestrictive adjective clause. Notice how the restrictive clause describing the word *bones* provides an important modification of the meaning. The nonrestrictive clause in the second example adds incidental, unimportant information.

Restrictive

According to John Hutchinson, an evolutionary biomechanist, gorilla bones **that grow to the size of King Kong's** would not have the structural strength to carry King Kong's weight.

Nonrestrictive

King Kong's bones, **which have fascinated biomechanist John Hutchinson,** would not have the structural strength to carry King Kong's weight.

Older grammar books require use of the word *that* for restrictive clauses and *which* for nonrestrictive. But in the past few years, writers have been using these two words interchangeably. Since usage patterns sometimes change, it is a good possibility that the older rule about *which* and *that* will soon be replaced. However, for clarity, use *that* for restrictive clauses and *which* for nonrestrictive clauses, as in these examples:

Restrictive

A San Francisco cable car **that was made from 270,836 matchsticks** is on exhibit in the San Francisco Ripley's Believe It or Not Museum.

Nonrestrictive

A San Francisco cable car, **which is a popular exhibit,** was made from 270,836 matchsticks and is on display in the San Francisco Ripley's Believe It or Not Museum.

Notice how the boldfaced clause in the restrictive example contains important information, while the clause in the nonrestrictive example contains incidental information. The word *which* and the use of commas indicate a nonrestrictive clause.

Other Additional Nonrestrictive Elements: Appositive Brush Strokes and Adjectives Out-of-Order

Two additional nonrestrictive structures are used to enrich images: appositive brush strokes and adjectives out-of-order. These two structures seldom cause a problem, but keep in mind that both are set off with commas, indicating a zoom lens added detail. While the added detail is not essential, it often adds to the power of the descriptive image. For examples, review Painting Brush Strokes in Section One.

Examine the article below and try to find examples of each of these errors: (1) dangling participles, (2) commas in a series, (3) agreement between pronoun and antecedent, (4) restrictive and nonrestrictive clauses. There are five places in the following article where these errors occur. Circle each error you find.

Global Warming: A Threat Greater Than Terrorism?

Not all scientists agree on the cause of global warming, but few deny its existence. Examining the wide range of data, our planet appears to be warming at an alarming rate. The Arctic ice thickness, for example, has shrunk from ten feet to six in less than 30 years. The Arctic surface ice has shrunk by 250 million acres—an area as large as California, Texas and Maryland combined.

Projections of the warming trend on our planet vary. Scientists believe by 2100 the earth's temperature could range anywhere from 2.5 to 10 degrees warmer. Each of these projections has their discouraging outcomes. However, all indicate that even the lowest projected temperature increase would create a chain reaction of warming ocean waters that would in turn lead to more frequent hurricanes.

Meteorologists note that the deadliest hurricanes which are category 4 and 5 have occurred in the last fifteen years. In that same time span, hurricanes have also increased in frequency. From 1970 until 1985, across the entire planet hurricanes averaged 10 per year. From 1990 until 2000 the average rate of hurricanes almost doubled, increasing to 18 per year.

Professor Peter Webster, MIT graduate and expert on atmospheric and ocean dynamics, believes the increased frequency of hurricanes was due to a rise in the ocean's temperature of only .5 degrees Fahrenheit. This slight rise in temperature has already caused the costly destruction of buildings the irreparable damage to coral reefs a dramatic increase in heat-triggered diseases and a significant number of coastal deaths. Consequently, futurists have suggested that global warming will eventually be recognized as a greater threat than terrorism.

—Written with included errors by Harry Noden

ACTIVITY 16 Showtime Performance

Musicians practice, experiment, and create before performing. Throughout this book, you have gone through a similar process as a writer. The Showtime Performance is an invitation to show what you've learned. With this activity, you will need to demonstrate your knowledge of various conventions and grammatical structures by using them.

Review the Showtime Performance Rubric on page 115 so that you know what your writing needs to include and how it will be evaluated. Then, follow the five steps necessary to complete this activity.

Writing and Revising the First Draft and Revision

1 On a piece of notebook paper, write a first draft description of the image on the right. Keep the pages in your activities book for your final draft.

2 Review your draft and revise where needed to include all style items listed on the Showtime Performance Rubric (numbers 1–7).

3 Write the name of each stylistic technique in the margin and draw a line to where you used it.

Proofreading for Common Errors

4 Proofread your draft for the selected types of grammatical errors listed (numbers 8–14).

5 Review the rubric one last time to be sure you've covered everything.

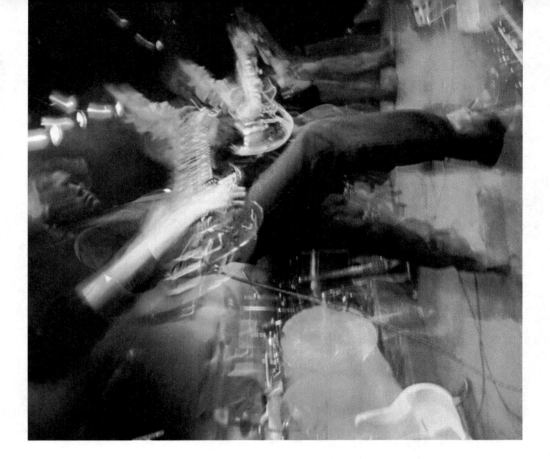

Name _____

Period _____

Name _____

Period _____

ACTIVITY 16 continued

Name

Period

Name _____ Period _____

Showtime Performance Rubric

You can earn 10 points for each item on this checklist.

Writing First Draft and Revision

Identify in the margin of your paper at least one of each of the following stylistic structures and draw a line from your label to the example.

_____ **1.** A Participle Brush Stroke

_____ **2.** Adjectives Out-of-Order

_____ **3.** An Absolute Brush Stroke

_____ **4.** An Appositive Brush Stroke

_____ **5.** Use of Specific Nouns and Verbs

_____ **6.** Parallel Structure (possibly with prepositional phrases)

_____ **7.** Action Verbs (no more than three linking verbs)

Proofreading Common Errors

Check your paper for each of the following structures. (You will receive 10 points for each type of error **not** found in your paper.)

_____ **8.** Dangling Participles

_____ **9.** Sentence Fragments

_____ **10.** Run-Ons

_____ **11.** Incorrect Use of Comma after an Introductory Element

_____ **12.** Breaking the Rhythm of Parallel Structure

_____ **13.** Incorrect Use of Commas in a Series

_____ **14.** Incorrect Use of Comma with a Restrictive Element

_____ = Total Points   Grade _____

ACTIVITY 17   Fumblerules

The errors you have examined in this section are so common that they have circulated on the Internet as Fumblerules—sentences that contain a violation of the very rule they identify as an error. Read these sentences and circle the error in each.

1. Verbs has to agree in number with their subjects.

2. Don't use no double negatives.

3. Just between you and I, the case of pronouns is important.

4. About sentence fragments. You should avoid them.

5. Don't use run-on sentences you must punctuate them.

6. Capitalize proper nouns like the mississippi river.

7. Set down and read this list.

8. Their the best burgers in town.

9. When writing an author should use commas for introductory elements.

10. Its important to use apostrophes right in everybodys writing.

11. Being bad grammar, a writer should not use dangling participles.

12. In letters essays and reports use commas to separate items in a series.

13. Make sure each pronoun agrees with their antecedent.

14. Commas shouldn't be used with items, that are restrictive.

Image Credits

122